Dale S. Higbee

FREUD'S
CONTRIBUTION
TO
PSYCHIATRY

FREUD'S CONTRIBUTION TO PSYCHIATRY

BY

A. A. BRILL, Ph.B., M.D.

W · W · NORTON & COMPANY · INC · *New York*

PRINTED IN THE UNITED STATES OF AMERICA
FOR THE PUBLISHERS BY THE VAIL-BALLOU PRESS

To Dr. Rose Owen Brill, my wife, who unwittingly inspired my quest for Freud's psychoanalysis, and whose patience and encouragement sustained me in the struggle to establish it in this country.

CONTENTS

PREFACE

THIS book represents the fruit of more than four decades of close application to psychiatry and thirty-seven years of active participation in the psychoanalytic movement. It is, broadly speaking, my psychiatric autobiography. I am recording here my personal experiences in a field of science into which I entered by chance on the threshold of its modern evolution. For in 1903 psychiatry was a poor and neglected field and, except for its somber shroud of mystery, held out few attractions for a hopeful medical neophyte.

Fortune had later thrown me into the Freudian world, wherein I have perforce collaborated in transmuting the old descriptive psychiatry into the dynamic science of today. I am attempting here to follow this important development as it unfolded itself on the psychiatric stage and as I have seen it from behind the scenes. For I am presumptuous enough to think that a knowledge of Freud's mode of approach to the study of mental processes will interest not alone psychiatrists, but students of every phase of human endeavor.

This work should not, however, be considered a compendium of everything that Freud has produced—it is rather a résumé of my own experiences in relation to what I consider the greatest epoch of psychopathology.

A. A. B.

New York, September, 1944

INTRODUCTORY REMARKS

FIRST, I wish to thank the committee, collectively and individually, for selecting me as the Salmon lecturer of 1943. It is a signal honor to be ranked with the distinguished men who have preceded me here and I am deeply appreciative of this honor. I was particularly moved by the words of my revered teacher, Dr. Adolf Meyer, who was the first Salmon lecturer and my first teacher of psychiatry.

In the fall of 1903, when I was a member of the first class of the New York State Hospital physicians to be trained by Dr. Meyer in the study and examination of mental patients, I was a raw recruit with only a few months of hospital experience. Dr. Meyer gave us a short but intensive course at the old Pathological Institute on Ward's Island, but his scheme of examination and systematic study of mental patients so impressed me that I have followed it imperatively ever since. Sometime later, it was my good fortune to take another more extensive course with Dr. Meyer. This time we were trained for the newly created position of pathologist which Dr. Meyer instituted in the New York State Hospitals. The thorough grounding in the techniques of histopathology, especially of the central nervous system, which Dr. Meyer and his able staff —Drs. Kirby, Macfie Campbell, Dunlop and Rusk—inculcated in us, taught me to appreciate the importance of the organic factors in nervous and mental diseases. Fate later directed my interest to the psychogenetic factors of the neuroses, yet throughout my whole career I have always followed the approach to psychiatry as taught by Dr. Meyer. I therefore take this opportunity to acknowledge here my deep gratitude to the benign and unassuming gentleman who introduced me this evening.

Dr. Meyer has also influenced me in the selection of the theme for these lectures. When Dr. C. C. Burlingame, the Chairman of the Salmon Committee, informed me that I was to be the Salmon lecturer of 1943, I did not know what topic to present here. To be sure, I am firmly identified with psychoanalysis. For a period of thirty-five years I have translated, written, discussed and argued psychoanalysis and fought for it extra- and intra-academically. But as this subject is still apt to stir up feelings in some superficially informed quarters, I thought seriously of speaking about something uncontroversial, something that is perhaps only remotely related to Freud and his teachings. However, a letter from Dr. Meyer, in which he said that he was looking forward with great interest to my Salmon lectures for a history of the facts and orientations of psychoanalytic contributions to psychiatry, decided the issue. I fully agree with Dr. Meyer that "there is a great need of going into the ideas and prospectives of the work in our field," and I shall, therefore, endeavor to present in these lectures the psychoanalytic contribution to psychiatry as I have observed it.

ONE

DESCRIPTIVE AND INTERPRETATIVE
PSYCHIATRY

ACCIDENTAL or, perhaps better, incidental factors, as I will show, put me in close touch with the origin and development of psychoanalysis, but in 1907, when I was first introduced to it, I had no idea that psychoanalysis would be considered something apart from psychiatry. For I came upon this to me entirely strange science through the portals of the Psychiatric Clinic in the City of Zurich, the birthplace of Dr. Meyer. In reflecting on the unconscious factors that so readily attracted me to this new field, it occurred to me that one of them was surely determined by my familiarity with the Swiss psychiatric scene, impressed upon me directly by Dr. Meyer and indirectly by my later study of Forel's work on hypnotism. Hence, when Dr. Frederick Peterson suggested in the summer of 1907 that I go to the Psychiatric Clinic headed by Bleuler and Jung, his advice sounded like the refrain of an old song. It was pleasing because it rang familiarly. Lest there be some misunderstanding, I must add that Dr. Meyer is not at all responsible for my later commissions. I know that Dr. Meyer was fully informed by C. G. Jung of my sojourn at Burghölzli and of my activities there, and he has naturally been fully cognizant of everything that had happened since then. But as a true scientist, Dr. Meyer has always looked at everything dispassionately. He was always ready to listen to anyone who had a message to deliver on anything relating to psychiatry.

I am dwelling on my psychiatric experiences prior to my espousing the cause of Freud in order to legitimatize myself, as it were, with those who have not known me as well as some of you. I wish to show that I did not maneuver myself into a psychoanalyst premeditatedly. During my New York State Hospital career, I had been an assiduous student of psychiatry and took full advantage of the opportunities offered there. I read my first psychiatric paper in October, 1905,[1] at a time when I almost became Kraepelin's translator. I was thus no novice in psychiatry when I later came to Zurich, as was shown by the fact that as soon as a vacancy occurred Dr. Bleuler appointed me an assistant in his hospital. I am proud to say that I was the only psychiatrist trained here who ever attained this distinction.

Some of you may feel that I have already talked enough about myself and may take it amiss if I should continue to use the first person singular in the delineation of the era that I am about to present. Let me, therefore, say that nothing is farther from my mind. I have no desire to boast of my own achievements, but as I am to discuss a very important contribution to a new era of psychiatric development in this country in which I have actively participated, I must perforce speak of my own experiences. Moreover, as I have always been a clinician, I see no objection to presenting my own case history as a participator in the psychiatric and psychoanalytic movement from 1903 to the present. After all, only that which is presented as exaggerated exploitations is malodorous. If, hereinafter, I am forced into the center of the picture, I shall nevertheless be surrounded by a strictly factual atmosphere. Furthermore, at the threshold of three score and ten, the impulse for self-glorification is surely on the wane, while the incentive to frankness is no longer deterred by fear of the future. Since 1907, I have devoted myself altogether to the practice and study of psychoanalytic psychiatry, and as psychoanalysis is one of the most important contributions to the psychiatric armamentarium, and as I am thoroughly familiar with it, having been on very friendly terms with its discoverer until his departure from life, I feel that I have something to tell which will be of interest to students of interpretative psychiatry.

The term "interpretative psychiatry" was first used by George H. Kirby in 1923, in his introduction to the English edition of Bleuler's *Textbook of Psychiatry*.[2] As I shall have many occasions to refer to this term, I think it best to quote exactly what Kirby

---

[1] A. A. Brill: "Psychic Epilepsy," *Long Island M. J.*, January, 1907.

[2] E. Bleuler: *Textbook of Psychiatry*, translated by A. A. Brill, Macmillan Co., 1924.

meant by it. Speaking of Bleuler's psychiatry as given in the text-book, Kirby states: "The book marks a notable advance in psychiatry in that it emphasizes sharply the contrast between the older descriptive psychiatry of Kraepelin and the new interpretative psychiatry of the present time which utilizes the psychoanalytic principles and the general biological viewpoints developed by Freud and his pupils in Europe, and by Meyer, Hoch, White and others in this country." [3]

This distinction between pure description and regulated interpretation impressed me forcibly soon after I came to the Burghölzli Clinic, and to make myself more explicit I will have to go into some details. As I said before, the foundation in psychiatry which I obtained from Dr. Meyer laid a great deal of stress on Kraepelin, whose name at that time shone resplendently in the psychiatric world. I cannot definitely recall that Dr. Meyer told us to read Kraepelin's work, but we all were told to read Allan Ross Diefendorf's work [4] which, according to this author, was only an abstract of Kraepelin's views. As soon as I began to earn money I bought Kraepelin's *Einführung in die psychiatrische Klinik*, a book of thirty clinics on the various forms of mental diseases. I was very much impressed by this work and I made a translation of each lecture as I read it for my own use and for some of my colleagues who could not read German. The latter were equally impressed and wished the book to be made accessible to English readers. Thereupon, I wrote to Kraepelin offering to become his translator. I received a very nice answer from him in which he said he had already given the translation rights to an English physician, Dr. Johnston. In due time, I also studied Kraepelin's major works [5] and thus deepened my knowledge of general psychiatry. These works were very comprehensive, very instructive, very interesting, but, as Dr. Kirby said, purely descriptive. Somewhat later, I studied also Wernicke's *Grundriss der Psychiatrie*, another work composed of clinical lectures. All these works were either directly recommended by Dr. Meyer or I took it for granted

---

[3] *Ibid.*, p. 7.
[4] *Clinical Psychiatry*, Macmillan Co., 1902.
[5] *Psychiatrie*, vols. I and II of the 6th German edition, 1899.

they were because they were frequently mentioned in his talks to us.

Right here I wish to state that Dr. Meyer's written abstracts and lectures were not restricted to theories of the authors mentioned, but from the very beginning he injected into them his own views. Thus, Kraepelin's two entities, dementia praecox and manic-depressive psychosis, which were then of paramount interest to the psychiatric world, gave rise to many controversial comments, as can be seen by reading the psychiatric literature of the time. Some denied the validity of these entities and some doubted their very existence. As is invariably the case in new concepts, many found it difficult, if not impossible, to fit every case into Kraepelin's framework, for some of the patients encountered in the hospital could be *hebephrenic, catatonic,* or *paranoid,* while others showed all these phases at different times. Nor could every case be classified as definitely dementia praecox or strictly manic-depressive psychosis. Dr. Meyer, with his flexible approach to psychiatry, soon added the classifications of "allied to dementia praecox" and "allied to manic-depressive psychosis," classifications that were not only most helpful to us beginners but that were also accepted later by other psychiatrists. Thus Bleuler's "schizoid-manic" classification, which he formulated many years later, corresponds essentially to Meyer's "allied to dementia praecox or manic-depressive psychosis." As I became better acquainted with theoretical psychiatry and with Dr. Meyer's later works, I realized that from the very beginning Dr. Meyer aimed to give us here—I mean in this country—a good general psychiatric foundation as well as a broader approach to the subject, an approach he later designated as psychobiological. But as I was with him, literally speaking, only a short period, and continually read psychiatric literature, particularly of the German school, I became more and more impressed by the descriptive psychiatry of Kraepelin.

However, in addition to my study of clinical psychiatry, I functioned also as the pathologist and bacteriologist of the hospital. I performed autopsies, collected and preserved neuropathological material for future study, and whenever I found anything that seemed interesting I consulted with some of the members of the Psychiatric Institute. As I was able to read psychiatry in a number of languages and as none of my colleagues could read anything but English, I got into the habit of translating interesting material from foreign neuropsychiatric periodicals and texts and reading some of it to the members of the staff for entertainment and discussion. Most of us were seriously striving for a clear and comprehensive understanding of what was to us a new science.

After serving as pathologist for more than two years, most of the time under trying conditions, I tired of the routine laboratory work and asked Dr. George A. Smith, the superintendent, to put me back to clinical work. I was then assigned as assistant on the reception service and a few months later was put in charge of it. After about two years of this work, I again became restless and noticed that my interest in the work was flagging. The main reason for this state of mind was the fact that I had found the girl of my choice and, desiring to marry, we decided not to remain in the hospital. For one thing, the housing facilities in the Central Islip Hospital were at that time inadequate for married existence and, having decided to go into private practice, I wondered how one could earn a livelihood practicing psychiatry. I reasoned that the great majority of patients I had encountered in the hospital could not be kept at home, and even if that were possible in some few cases, I wondered what one could do for them. For the most important labor in the hospital, even in the reception service, was the initial examination of the patients which usually filled from ten to fifteen typewritten pages. It consisted of both a physical and neuropsychiatric examination, adequate enough for a diagnosis and usually also for a differential diagnosis. But once this was accomplished, the patient was transferred to an appropriate ward where the doctor in charge continued the notes from time to time as the occasion demanded.

I might remark that the notes of the pre-Meyerian period were hardly worthy of the name. It might interest you to hear how they actually read. Here is an example: "John Doe, 26, single, laborer, was admitted on January 15, 1884. He was excitable, delusional, shouting and screaming." About a year or so later, the second note read: "The patient is stupid, dull and demented." Some years later, there was a note by another physician which read: "Patient continues as above." A year or so later: "Patient is stupid, dull and demented." Four or five years later: "Patient is demented, dull and stupid." If the patient continued to live twenty or more years, the various doctors in charge vied with one another in making new permutations and combinations of the original "dull, stupid and demented" note. Then there was the final note: "Patient died suddenly."

With the advent of Dr. Meyer, the notes had to be written at short intervals, they had to be logical and, above all, they had to tell something about the patient. However, in contrast to the progress in examination and study, the treatment consisted mostly of "watchful waiting," the medications depending on the symptoms. If the patient was depressed, he received tonics; if excited, sedatives, hypnotics, narcotics, or some form of physical restraint. As most of this sort of treatment seemed unfeasible outside of hospitals, I had every reason to worry about the prospects of earning a livelihood in the private practice of psychiatry.

But as necessity is the mother of "reflection," I began to think of the borderline cases of mental disease, neurasthenias and hysterias, and their psychotherapeutic treatment, concerning which I had read but knew very little. For at the beginning of this century, the whole psychiatric apparatus consisted of hyoscine, morphine, chloral, paraldehyde, and hydro- and electrotherapy, which were administered, as occasion demanded, in hospitals, clinics and in private practice, regardless of whether one dealt with organic or functional disorders. In brief, the treatment of the psychoses and neuroses was very barren to say the least and, with a few notable exceptions, few physicians gave any serious thought to the borderline cases of mental diseases. They were invariably classified as hysteria, psychasthenia, or neurasthenia; the first concept was usually restricted to what the French school designated as major hysteria, the second included not only the compulsive states but also mild schizophrenia, while neurasthenia covered everything that could not be explained on an organic basis. Neurasthenia was truly the garbage can of mental medicine, as Forel aptly called it, and once this diagnosis was made, the patient was often discredited as a malingerer and treated by means of placebos, "jollies" as we called them. He was told to forget his complaints. If some conscientious physician took such a patient seriously, he treated him symptomatically.

This attitude prevailed during the first two decades of this century, and still exists in some quarters. Thus, in the Neurological Department of the Vanderbilt Clinic, Dr. Starr would never diagnose a case as hysteria unless the patient showed anesthesias of the pharynx and cornea, as well as other major hysterical manifestations. As to the all-inclusiveness of neurasthenia at that time, let me cite the following episode: I was once asked by the Chief of the Neurological Clinic, Dr. Cunningham, to gather suitable cases for Professor Starr's Clinic on Neurasthenia. Knowing his views on the subject, I asked what kind of cases he wanted and he said: "All functional cases that have not too many hallucinations and delusions." It made no difference to Dr. Cunningham whether we dealt with neurasthenia, hysteria, compulsion neurosis, or some incipient organic disease not yet pronounced enough to be diagnosed as dementia praecox or general paresis. No thought was given to psychic treatment; depending upon his complaints, the patient received either a sedative or tonic which was prescribed in accordance with the Vanderbilt Clinic Formulary under the letter C— "Mixtures for Diseases of the Nervous System." [6] The whole concept of treatment was still based on the old adage *mens sana in corpore sano* in the sense that if the patient were physically sound, he would not have a neurasthenia, psychasthenia, or hysteria.

As I had already had enough experience to place little faith in such symptomatic treatment, I naturally thought of psychotherapy. But all that I knew about it at that time was that psychotherapy meant mental therapy with special reference to hypnotism and suggestion. Today there is at least one psychotherapist in every moderate-sized city. In big centers, as well as in most of the psychiatric hospitals, there are trained psychiatrists who devote most, if not all, of their time to some form of psychotherapy. But before 1900, there were no physicians who specialized in mental therapy or who called themselves psychotherapists.

[6] The same situation existed in all clinics and dispensaries of New York City.

Today psychotherapy is a vast realm. It comprises hypnotism, suggestion, education, and persuasion, the different schools of psychoanalysis, Adolf Meyer's psychobiology, vocational therapy, music therapy, religious therapy in the form of Christian Science and the Emmanuel movement, as well as different forms of group therapy. But not even the word *psychotherapy* is found in any of the psychiatric works of Clouston, Paton, White, Weygand, or Bianchi, which were published, here and abroad, at the beginning of this century. I was more than surprised to find no reference to psychotherapy in the 1935 edition of Jelliffe and White's *Diseases of the Nervous System.* To be sure, there are indirect references and allusions to what we might now call psychotherapy in many of the old works on mental diseases, as well as on medicine in general; but psychotherapy as such was practically unknown.

However, when I began to think seriously of studying psychotherapy, I immediately thought of hypnotism. It was not what I read about the subject in the psychiatric literature that drew me to it in the first place, for most of my serious reading on the subject was done after I had decided to take it up as a vocation. Hypnotism was brought to my mind a number of times before 1905–6. One of the first, if not the first, English novel I read was Du Maurier's *Trilby*, in which the hypnotist, Svengali, makes a vocal star of a poor artist's model. This novel was a best-seller toward the end of the last century and I was particularly impressed by it. A few years later while a junior in college, I dabbled in hypnotism with my psychology teacher, and in 1902, during my last year in the College of Physicians and Surgeons, I was recommended by the dean's office to Dr. Boris Sidis, a well-known pioneer in this field, when he sought an assistant for his experiments in hypnotism in the New York Infirmary for Women and Children. These incidents undoubtedly were the unconscious determinants for my later interest in hypnotism.

Once I had made my decision, I read diligently whatever literature I could find on the subject. I was particularly impressed by Forel's *Hypnotismus* which at that time enjoyed great popularity. I tried hard to master the technique and as soon as I dared, I applied it to some of the accessible patients in the hospital. I soon learned that self-taught techniques leave much to be desired, although, as I found out later, my experience with hypnotism was not different from that of many others. Some patients were hypnotizable and it was a pleasure to see them "go under" and obey my command suggestions, while others could not be made to fall asleep. When I persistently cajoled such a patient to close his eyes and go to sleep, and finally said assuringly, "Now you are asleep," the patient just opened his or her eyes and said: "No, doctor, I am not asleep." That was very disconcerting. When it happened the first time, I was naturally chagrined and more or less confused, not knowing just what to say. But after many similar experiences, I tried to save my face by haltingly remarking that I did not mean real sleep. I thus behaved like the Delphian oracle whose statements were doubtful enough to be construed in many ways.

Just then I came upon another psychotherapy. I refer to Dubois's *The Psychic Treatment of Nervous Disorders,*[7] which had recently appeared in English form. This book not only taught me a new method of psychotherapy, but in reading reviews and criticisms of it I was initiated into a new phase of psychiatric life, namely, the controversial aspect of its various schools. Being still quite "green," I was shocked by the academic bout between Dr. Dubois and the hypnotherapists. I had no idea at that time that I was soon to become embroiled in the most celebrated *odium psychiatricum.*

Dubois was set against hypnotic therapy, as will be shown by the following words: [8] "The psychotherapy which I call rational has no need of this sort of preparatory narcosis of hypnosis, or of this sort of hypersuggestibility, that is itself suggested. It is not addressed to an impressionable polygon, but simply to the mind and the reason of the subject. This psychic therapy is indicated in all the affections in which one recognizes the influence of mental ideas and they are legion." Dubois based his psychotherapy entirely on education or re-education of the patient. He rejected all expressions of *authority,* which, he claimed, is always bad in spite

[7] Translated by Jelliffe and White, 1905.
[8] *Ibid.,* p. 233.

of its momentary success because it does not conduce the necessary clear-sightedness. He was also against all forms of *suggestion*, because he said that it, too, crushes the spirit and develops a great field which is inherent in the human mind, that is, suggestibility. Dubois recognized only one means of education and that was *persuasion* by means of proof, by demonstration, by logical induction, and by reason which touches the heart.[9]

Thus admitting that suggestibility is inherent in the mind, Dubois nevertheless imagined that it could be entirely eliminated. Dubois's psychotherapeutic method cannot be mastered by reading his work—at least I could not do it. The only interest that I find in Dubois is his rejection of hypnotism because it is based on authority. Freud, too, revolted against what he called the violence of hypnotism, but mainly because it did not allow any insight into the nature and origin of the symptoms. From what I could grasp of Dubois's work, it seemed monotonous, vague, and often confusing. I did, however, strive hard in 1905–6 to master it because I entertained a high regard for Jelliffe and White, the translators, and because I wished to fill the hiatus of unhypnotizability. However, my many efforts to make practical use of this method of persuasion usually ended in failure. I well recall how I once tried it on a patient who had been suffering for some time from loud, tic-like belchings which, once started, continued for hours. After I had reasoned with this simple individual for about an hour, he looked puzzled and continued to belch as loudly as ever. I then became irritated at what I considered his stupidity and tried hypnotism, to which he readily succumbed. It was then quite easy to remove his symptom by direct command. I ordered him to stop belching and when he continued, I just yelled, "Shut up!" and he finally did; I then commanded that he must never do it again. My own omnipotence of thought was obviously better attuned to the direct approach of hypnotism, through which I obtained some successful results—if the patient were willing. As I said previously, not all patients were willing, and what was still more upsetting was the fact that the results were only transitory.

While I was thus striving hard to improve my technique, I read

[9] *Psychotherapy*, vol. II, Center Publishing Co., 1909.

one day in the daily press that a certain Dr. John D. Quackenbos
worked miraculous cures by hypnotism.[10] I found out later that
Dr. Quackenbos had been practicing hypnotism in New York for
a number of years. I had never heard of him because his writings,
which were quite profuse, rarely appeared in the neuropsychiatric
journals. As he was kind enough to grant me an interview, I took
a day off from the hospital and called on him. I was mainly interested in how to become efficient enough to hypnotize all of my
patients. Dr. Quackenbos was a fine-appearing, cultured gentleman, more or less of the Svengali type. He listened to me smilingly
as I recited my shortcomings as a hypnotist, and then led me to
a good-sized room which was divided into cubicles and there I saw
patients stretched out on cots, fast asleep and snoring. I said to
him admiringly, "How do you do it?" He then informed me that
at first he had experienced the same difficulties that I had encountered, but that he had solved the problem by giving up the idea of
putting patients to sleep solely by verbal suggestion. He said: "If
they don't succumb to suggestive sleep, I just give them a stiff
dose of paraldehyde and they soon 'go under.' " He assured me that
the appropriate suggestions imparted under these conditions were
just as efficacious. As he spoke and I sensed the pungent odor of
that familiar drug which we so generously dispensed to our hospital patients at that time, the doctor's Svengalilike figure suddenly underwent a marked shrinkage in my sight. However, as
time went on and I had more experience with psychotherapy, I
have often thought more charitably, nay admiringly, of Dr.
Quackenbos. Like many pioneers in a new field, he was perhaps
somewhat oversanguine about the results of his work, but there is
no question about his honesty of purpose. Another pioneer who
made very valuable contributions in this field, Dr. Boris Sidis, complained in 1910 that whereas the leading medical journals in this
country were quite willing to publish papers on constipation and
kindred disturbances, they invariably rejected articles on hypnotism and on psychopathological subjects.[11] I can only add that

[10] John D. Quackenbos: *Hypnotic Therapeutics*, New York, Harper and
Brothers.
[11] *Psychotherapeutics, a Symposium*, the Gorham Press, 1910.

the rank and file of physicians are still quite skeptical about everything that concerns the mind.

However, as I was still in quest of a better psychotherapeutic
technique, I took a leave of absence from the hospital and jour-
neyed to Paris in the spring of 1907. Like many others before and
after me, I went there because the literature on hypnotism was
centered around the famous figure of Charcot, despite the fact
that Charcot was neither the first to recognize the value of hypnotism in medicine nor the one who made the best use of it. Still,
the fact that Jean Martin Charcot, the well-known psychiatrist and
neurologist, saw fit to utilize this method which had hitherto been
rejected and tabooed by the rank and file of European scientists,
and that he left interesting, nay, fascinating works about his experiments with it in the Salpêtrière—all that made him most prominent in any serious discussion on hypnotism. There was a woman
physician in the hospital, Dr. Leader, who had a copy of Charcot's
lectures, and when she heard that I was interested in hypnotism,
she was kind enough to give me the book. There is something in
the written word, especially if it conveys ideas clearly, that sur-
passes any other mode of expression. Truly, in the beginning
there was the Logos! and reading these lectures I became en-
raptured by Charcot's case records and experiments in the Salpêtrière and decided to go there someday.

Those who are acquainted with the life of Sigmund Freud will
recall that almost a generation before, in 1885, he, too, was attracted to Paris and worked a year with Charcot in the Salpêtrière.
Some have even suggested that there was something peculiar that
I should have followed in the same path. There is nothing supernatural or even strange about this coincidence. At the turn of the
century, every psychiatrist who wished to perfect himself in
psychopathology thought of Paris and the Salpêtrière, just as every
physician of this country who wished to specialize in diseases of
the eye, ear, nose, and throat thought of Vienna. I knew nothing
about Freud when I went to Paris, and if I had ever come across
his name in psychiatric literature, which is quite possible, it surely
had left no conscious memory in me. Sometime after I had learned
about Freud and his views, I recalled that his name was mentioned

to me in 1905 under rather peculiar circumstances. Accidentally, I met an Austrian artillery lieutenant in Belgium during a visit to the exhibition in Liége. We happened to sit at the same table in a restaurant and thus became acquainted. We then traveled together for a few days and when we parted we expressed the hope of meeting again someday. I remarked that I expected to visit Europe in 1907–8 and that I would probably go to Paris. He thereupon said, "Why don't you come to Vienna and study with Freud?" When I asked, "Who is Freud?" he answered: "Oh, he must be somebody; else he would not have so many opponents."

Charcot had been dead about fifteen years by the time I reached Paris and I was surprised and disappointed that most of the neu-rologists and psychiatrists whom I met during the first week no longer believed in the efficacy of hypnotism and suggestion. Some had much good to say about a new method to which they referred as *isolation*. It was a sort of modified Weir Mitchell rest cure. Later when I had an opportunity to be alone with one of these patients *in isolation*, I was amused to hear what she thought of it. As no one was permitted to talk to her, she was quite pleased to converse with me. I discovered that she had gone through a number of these isolation "cures" and that she was always the one to say when she was well. She said that when she became bored and no longer en-joyed her isolation, she asked for her discharge, and the doctors were very *gentils* about it.

After looking through the clinics, I decided to enter the Hôspice de Bicêtre in Pierre Marie's service. I knew him through his works on acromegaly and aphasia. He was, besides, a charming gentleman and very hospitable when I introduced myself. I soon found that a number of American psychiatrists had been there before. Thus, I was amused to see a caricature of Dr. Charles Macfie Campbell, who had worked there for some time before he came here to Adolf Meyer, on one of the walls of the dining room or the *salle de gare*. Pierre Marie suggested that I study a case of acromegaly with convulsive states. The neurological division in which I worked contained a wealth of material, mostly chronic cases of all types. The interns wittily designated this wing of the hospital, which had been built before the French Revolution, as "Siberia," because it was so dismal and so badly heated. The psychiatric division was dingy and rather poorly equipped, and to one accustomed to an entirely different environment, the contrast was very depressing.

The first time I accompanied the chief on his rounds I discovered that the patients were still classified as in the time of Pinel. Being quite chauvinistic, the French psychiatrists had no use for the Kraepelinian concepts. I was, therefore, somewhat pleased that I was in the neurological service. But as my object in coming to Paris had been to study psychopathology and especially psychotherapy, I was terribly disappointed but strove to make the best of an unpalatable situation. I devoted considerable time to my case of acromegaly, and whenever he began to show signs of convulsions, I made copious notes. But I became daily more dissatisfied, and in my despair I communicated with Dr. Frederick Peterson, who originally introduced me to psychiatry. I told him that I was thoroughly disillusioned, and that I was thinking of perhaps giving up psychiatry and going to Vienna for a course in nose and throat work. Dr. Peterson answered me promptly. He encouraged me to remain a psychiatrist and advised me to go to the clinic of psychiatry at Zurich, Switzerland. He spoke enthusiastically of the research carried on there with associations and the galvanometer, and then added: "They are testing Freud's theories by applying them to the psychoses which, I think, will interest you." Peterson had been there recently for about two months and worked with Jung on the "Psychogalvanic Investigations with the Galvanometer and Pneumograph in Normal and Insane Individuals." [12]

Frederick Peterson maintained his enthusiasm for psychoanalysis for many years. When I returned to New York with the English translation of Jung's *Psychology of Dementia Praecox*, in which Jung confirmed Freud's theories of dementia praecox, Peterson expressed his wish to be a cotranslator of it, and the first edition was published under both our names. In a paper, "The Electric Psychometer," [13] Peterson, speaking of the study of association in

[12] *Brain*, July, 1907.
[13] *Medical Record*, 1907.

the mind of man carried out by Jung, stated: "I have not observed anything thus far in my *Studienreise* that has interested me quite as much, and I felt that I should at once place the matter before my colleagues as a new field for their research, a new avenue by which to approach the secrets of the nervous system." But in 1919 he seems to have suddenly discovered that psychoanalysis was all wrong. It is of interest that for about two years I was his office associate, giving most if not all my time to analysis of cases that were selected by him. We were on friendly terms when I left his office, which was because I needed all my time for my own patients, and he then referred patients to my office for many years. But one day in 1919 he asked me to meet him and informed me of his intention to write against analysis, at the same time assuring me that he was convinced that, in the right hands, psychoanalysis was a valuable instrument. He felt it his duty to oppose psycho-analysis because it was highly abused by a number of unscrupulous physicians, some of whose names he mentioned. To my argument that he had no right to condemn a valuable technique just because some misused or abused it, he had only vague answers. I was well aware of the true reason for this *volte-face* but as I was much indebted to him and had a great fondness for him, I thought it best not to discuss it any further.

Peterson and I remained good friends until the end of his days. As he grew older and withdrew from his erstwhile numerous activities, the world gradually lost sight of him, and for years before he died, only a few thought of our indebtedness to this great benefactor of psychiatry, not only in this state but in the country. For it was mainly through his efforts that the organization and establishment of the Craig Colony for Epileptics came into being. He devoted more than ten years to the molding of this institution into a highly accredited hospital and a model of its kind. Nowadays few people realize that it was Peterson who, as soon as he became the Chairman of the New York State Commission in Lunacy (now the Department of Mental Hygiene), appointed Adolf Meyer as director of the New York Psychiatric Institute. Peterson reorganized the whole administrative system of our State Department of Mental Hygiene. It was Peterson also who appointed William L. Russell to the newly created position of Inspector of the New York State Hospitals, a position which has functioned ever since to the mutual benefit of patients and hospitals. It was also Peterson who urged the late Dr. Allan Ross Diefendorf to make a translation of Kraepelinian theories, and the resultant work, *Clinical Psychiatry*, though only an abstract of Kraepelin's work, was the only modern psychiatry in this country at the beginning of this century. Every progressive man in the state hospitals possessed a copy of it.[14] And, last but not least, Dr. Peterson worked hard for many years to influence the United States Department of Public Health to institute psychiatric examinations of aliens at the various immigration stations, and when this was finally put into operation, Dr. Peterson recommended Dr. Thomas W. Salmon, an assistant physician in the Willard State Hospital, as the first psychiatrist for Ellis Island. As one of his students in 1902–3, I remember well how Peterson strove to inculcate in us a sympathetic interest in psychiatry which at that time was held in general disrepute by the students and the medical profession. In his clinics he never failed to stress the fact that the state hospitals contained an abundance of good clinical and surgical material and that there was a good future for those students who would take up psychiatry as a specialty. Ergo, so far as the present speaker is concerned, Peterson not only introduced him to psychiatry but was also responsible for his espousing Freud's cause. Some, like Dr. Bernard Sachs, may consider this act as Peterson's one flagrant sin; if that is so, it is surely counteracted by his many virtues.

At all events, following Peterson's suggestion, I took a few days from my light duties at Bicêtre and traveled to Zurich. It was midsummer and Burghölzli, though at first sight somber in its mountainous surroundings, made a very fine impression on me. The genial director, Eugen Bleuler, and his very active *Sekundararzt*, or first assistant physician, Dr. C. G. Jung, received me kindly and were pleased to hear that I wished to work with them. I shall never forget the first staff meeting which I witnessed on that morning. I was puzzled and spellbound by what I saw and heard there. The

[14] This information was given to me by Dr. Diefendorf shortly after Peterson's death when I was gathering material for his obituary.

case presented that morning was a woman of about fifty years, whose disorder was clinically diagnosed as an "involution melancholia." If I had presented such a patient in New York, no matter how well I might have elaborated upon the morbid picture, I would not have gone beyond a thorough description of the onset and development of the symptoms. This part of the case history did not take up much time in Burghölzli. Dr. Bleuler, who conducted the examination, puzzled me by his approach to the patient. It was brought out, for example, that shortly before admission to the hospital, the patient had on a few occasions poured red wine into her bed before retiring. To me, at that time, this was only a peculiar action which one was wont to observe in such patients. In Burghölzli, after prolonged questioning, this act was construed as an effort on the part of the patient to re-establish her discontinued menstrual flow.

I noticed also that while talking to the patient, Bleuler raised her hands to his nose and smelled them. I was mystified by his action, but being a stranger I did not dare ask for an explanation. It soon turned out, however, that there was a question whether the patient was masturbating and that the odor of her hands might give the clue. I was naturally much impressed by the novelty and frankness that characterized the whole procedure. In New York we rarely discussed sex at staff meetings and if we had to do it sometimes, we all reacted to the situation with a certain amount of reserve, if not disgust. I could not help recalling a patient in Central Islip who had made sexual advances to his sister. Despite the fact that it was a dementia praecox, the members of the staff reacted with marked disgust to my reading of the case record. I naturally contrasted this with the matter-of-fact approach to the sexual life of the Zurich case. When I spoke of it later to Jung, he said: "The trouble with you is that you know nothing about Freud and his concepts on sex." Before leaving, he advised me to study Freud's *Traumdeutung* (The Interpretation of Dreams) and his *Psychopathologie des Alltagslebens* (The Psychopathology of Everyday Life).

I should have been glad to have been able to remain in Burghölzli then and there, but I had to get my effects from Paris and also felt obliged to wind up my study of the case of acromegaly in Bicêtre. When I returned to Burghölzli within a few weeks, my psychiatric interest was, as it were, "revivified." It was inspiring to be in a group of active and enthusiastic workers who were all toiling to master the Freudian principles and to apply them to the study of patients. Psychoanalysis seemed to pervade everything there. When one made a mistake in talking, he was immediately asked to explain it, and the frankness that was displayed on such occasions was truly amazing. Here was a group of experienced psychiatrists, Bleuler, Jung, Riklin, Abraham, and Hans Meier, all working overtime in order to find something new. At the time of my visit, they all seemed convinced that the Freudian mechanisms existed in every patient. Bleuler was not yet convinced of Freud's sexual concepts, but Jung and most of the others seemed to have accepted everything. Jung was the most enthusiastic Freudian of the group; he was so positive of everything that he brooked no differences of opinion when it concerned any Freudian theory.

The Zurich school—for they were known by this name—instigated by Bleuler, decided to investigate the Freudian theories through the methods of association. This investigation had started about six months before I came to Burghölzli and was in full swing when I arrived. Every assistant, in addition to his regular work, spent many hours daily performing association experiments on both normal and psychopathic individuals. Before I was regularly appointed to the staff, I spent all my time taking associations with galvanometric reading. Later on, when I had charge of the male service, I still gave at least two to three hours daily to association experiments. I was naturally curious to know why this whole movement was started, and, on inquiry, I got the following explanation: Kraepelin introduced new life into psychiatry by his close observation of his patients for long years. Being an independent and daring thinker, he shattered the traditions of centuries with his new classification of the psychoses. As a pupil of Wundt, he applied new methods of clinical investigation drawn from psychology. He combined mania and melancholia into a single disorder under the heading of manic-depressive psychosis, a concept that maintained itself despite vigorous attack. But the situation was different in the case of dementia praecox to which there were many valid objections, chiefly because of its all inclusiveness.

Thus, Kraepelin himself divided dementia praecox into three forms, the hebephrenic, the catatonic, and the paranoid, and intimated that in time it would probably be broken up still further into groups or types. Yet he deserved great credit for having placed before the psychiatric world a sort of psychological species, even if its outlines were gross and its details more or less obscure. In the main, however, Kraepelin has furnished only a general and superficial aspect of a new morbid entity. From his descriptions of dementia praecox, one learned that such patients are peculiar in speech and actions, that they utter senseless remarks, repeat meaningless words or syllables, and that now and then they commit foolish and impulsive acts; but Kraepelin made no attempt to examine the nature and origin of these peculiar expressions. Thus, reading Kraepelin's own case reports, one finds that whereas most of them showed hallucinations and delusions, these were not at all of the same content or nature; the verbigerations and mannerisms, too, differed in different cases. As this state of affairs was found everywhere, in every hospital, and as Freud had already shown [15] that a psychosis such as "chronic paranoia" was based on the same mechanisms as hysteria, it was only logical to test his theories in dementia praecox. After mature reflection, it was decided that the most direct and logical way of investigation would be by way of the association paths. As Bleuler put it: "The whole psychic existence of the past and the present with all its experiences and strivings is mirrored in the association activity. It is, therefore, an index of all psychic processes, which we must decipher in order to know the total man." [16] Moreover, as Freud based his whole technique on what he called free associations, it was only logical to start with the association experiment.

The importance of association of ideas has been duly recognized by all serious students of the mind. Zilboorg[17] gives Vives the

[15] *Neurologisches Centralblatt*, No. 10, 1896.
[16] *Diagnostische Assoziationsstudien*, Leipzig, Barth, 1906.
[17] *A History of Medical Psychology*, p. 192.

credit for having been the first to point out and describe the importance of psychological associations at the beginning of the sixteenth century. But its use in psychology undoubtedly dates from Wundt and his pupils, and in psychopathology from Kraepelin and Aschaffenburg. However, the association experiments of Bleuler and Jung differed in many respects from those of other investigators in the field. Through the "complex theory" and the "free association" method of Freud, the Zurich school demonstrated why we find different combinations of symptoms in different patients suffering from the same disease, and thus not only confirmed Freud's theories but inaugurated a new epoch in psychiatry—the method of interpretative psychiatry.

In my effort to legitimatize myself as a cicerone of the Freudian scene, I have at the same time endeavored to sketch briefly the status of psychiatry in the State of New York at the beginning of this century. Looking backward as one who was born, as it were, into the new psychiatric era, accouched by the indomitable and careful hands of Adolf Meyer, I feel that this was the greatest upsurge in scientific psychiatry in this country. I am glad that I was reared in it. But like all children, I was at first very anxious to remain at home with father. While I took my second course in the Institute, Dr. Meyer spoke to me about remaining there as one of his assistants. I should have been happy to do so, but for some reason this did not come to pass; the fates had decreed otherwise, But having been left to my own self, I have also retained the freedom of pursuing my own bent. When I grew psychiatrically older and restless, I could change from pathology to clinical psychiatry, and when I was still discontented, there was nothing to prevent me from starting my odyssey which finally led me to Freud.

Protagoras, the Sophist, who lived in the fifth century B.C., said that man is the most helpless of all creatures, and the only weapon he possesses against the innumerable dangers threatening him is his mind. Psychiatry has amply demonstrated what this Greek philosopher observed so long ago. Thus, Eugen Bleuler speaking of the mind says: "The psyche is the essential element in man, not only from a religious but also from the viewpoint of the natural sciences. Strong muscles and solid bones are still agreeable attributes for those who possess them, but one can direct a world without even having arms and legs, while a slight disturbance of the mind can change the strongest man into a pitiable object of care or into a dangerous enemy of society." [18]

There is no need to demonstrate the truth of these statements to psychiatrists. However, we are interested not only in the psychic development of man in so far as it enabled him to survive the trials and vicissitudes of millennia and emerge victorious, even, as Thornton Wilder puts it, "by the skin of our teeth," but we are particularly interested in the actual behavior of the psychic forces in mental disturbances and retrogressions produced by dangers from without. Descriptive psychiatry told us nothing about these. They became clear to me, however, as I continued to work in Burghölzli. I was captivated by the case histories because the patient no longer represented something entirely foreign to me, something insane, as I had hitherto regarded him when I merely described his strange behavior. Now even his most peculiar expressions as I traced them back to his former normal life struck familiar chords in me.

At first this slightly alarmed me. I feared lest there be something wrong with me; but I soon discovered that what I found in a patient, even while deciphering obsessions or delusions, was only an exaggerated or distorted expression of that which exists in every normal person. Since nothing is so convincing as that which one finds in oneself, my faith in the Freudian mechanisms was soon established. My colleagues, who had gone through the same experiences long before, were often amused at my enthusiasm. But we all felt that Freud gave us the microscope with which to examine the mind. Instead of a set of abnormal manifestations which seemingly had no relation to normal behavior, as we had hitherto been in the habit of seeing in every neurotic or psychotic patient, we now searched for the threads that led directly from the symptoms to something in the patient's former life that determined or gave origin to the symptoms.

Let me illustrate this by a simple example. A patient suffered

[18] Bleuler: *op. cit.*, p. 226.

from a ticlike upward sweep of his arms which appeared numerous times daily before he was sufficiently aware of it to try to control it. Such senseless motions of the tic variety are not uncommon in neuropsychiatric practice, and before Freud came on the scene no one thought of explaining them, or if one tried to do so, he usually attributed them to some irritation in the brain or nerves. As a rule, there was no logic to such explanations and even if there was a slight semblance of it, no one attributed any meaning to it. At best, such a patient received a sedative to calm his nerves. But the free-association method soon showed that this senseless motion represented an effort of the patient to ward off an idea, an obsessive thought that *God* might get into him. The patient dared not tell this to the examiner lest he be considered crazy, and it was only after considerable effort and time that it was elicited. But what does this strange obsession "God might get into me" mean? At first it sounds like some mystic idea, but the patient was a matter-of-fact mechanic and only moderately religious; he himself attributed no such feelings to it. He recalled that this idea gradually began to obsess him and finally became extremely annoying to him. After a few months, this senseless idea disappeared but instead he began the ticlike upward sweep of the arms just described. Further investigation by free associations brought to light the following episode which I shall briefly describe.

This patient was a single man of twenty-six years, a precision-instrument mechanic by occupation. To his coworkers in the factory, he was known as a reserved, timid and prudish individual who was easily shocked by any allusions to sex. Knowing this, they took advantage of his sensitiveness by frequently playing some trick or joke on him. A number of years before I saw him, some of his coworkers asked him to look out of the shop window and, pointing to two dogs *in coitu* in the yard below, said laughingly, "How would you like to be the top dog?" He reacted to this scene with marked embarrassment, to the great amusement of his tormentors. But try as he would, he was unable to banish the scene from his eyes, nor could he stop hearing the words, "How would you like to be the top dog?" As time went on and this image obsessed him, he was forced to repeat in his mind, "No, you are not going to be the top dog; you are not going to be the top dog." And as is invariably the case in obsessive neurotics, he defended himself against this sensual thought by repeating to himself, "No, you are not going to be the top dog; you are not going to get into the dog." In time these obsessions were replaced by the ticlike motion of the arms which represented the same defense reaction without the words or disagreeable images. The patient then thought that this upward sweep was a defense reaction to the compulsive thought "God might get into me," that it was a way to keep God from getting into him.

The key to this whole obsession, however, is found when we know that the word "God" is a kind of palindrome, which, read backward, is "dog." [19] In other words, instead of obsessively speculating about the sensual idea of sexual intercourse, which was evoked by the sight of the dogs, the disagreeable scene and the words connected with it were gradually pushed out of consciousness; they were repressed into the unconscious. Had they remained there undisturbed, there would have been no neurotic symptom. Instead, the dynamic repressed material constantly strove to come to the surface and, as the repression failed, the forgotten material came up by a devious path distorted into an obsession which, though more agreeable to this very prudish individual, was nevertheless just as annoying to him as a neurotic symptom. Later, I shall discuss the psychodynamics of the obsession and show that this peculiar symptom developed because the patient was assailed by dangers from without.

In a critical review of a paper by Moebius, Dr. Adolf Meyer makes the following assertions which I feel are apropos of this case.[20] Speaking of miscarried mental activities which are quite often at the center of the disorder for which the patient seeks help, Dr. Meyer dilates upon it as follows: "Certain unusual mental events appear and others fail to take place, and the result is an inability to meet the demands which would be met by normal

---

[19] Such inverted formations are not uncommon in neurotic and psychotic symptoms.

[20] "Misconceptions at the bottom of 'Hopelessness of All Psychology,'" *Psychological Bulletin*, IV, 170–179, 1907.

mental reaction. Like all other *biological* provisions or developments, the mental mechanisms meet, or fail to meet, definite kinds of biological demands, and the legitimate question is: what is the type of demand, and what is the mechanism or type of reaction that meets it? Further, since there are evidently degrees of efficiency in this function as in all others, we legitimately ask: which are the conditions for the proper working of this function and what are the ways of influencing it, if it threatens to miscarry?" Dr. Meyer laconically but masterfully described the nucleus of the problem of the neurosis and psychosis as we find it in our neuropsychiatric practice. And if we consider the compulsion neurotic previously described, we can say that etiologically he fits in every way into Dr. Meyer's description. The patient encountered what were to him certain unusual biological demands which he was unable to meet adequately because he lacked the necessary means for normal mental reaction. As to the type of demand and the mechanism or type of reaction that it met, the conditions that would have caused proper functioning, as well as the modes of preventing such a miscarriage—all these questions I will endeavor to answer later.

Before proceeding with these discussions, let us cast a glance at the history of psychotherapy which I feel will give a better comprehension of what is to follow. We must assume that some sort of psychotherapy was practiced long before history. We know from various sources of antiquity that in the beginning no distinction was made between physical and psychic maladies, although the parallel evolution of mind and body had occupied speculative mankind from the very beginning of civilization. Nevertheless, it is safe to assume that during the childhood of medicine, as we find it in Assyria, Babylonia, Egypt, India, Judea, Phoenicia, Greece, China, and ancient America, the prevailing concept of disease—mental or physical—was that it resulted from some demoniacal influence. The physician and the priest were embodied in the same person, and the same situation still exists among semi-enlightened and primitive peoples. Like the experienced Egyptian or Chaldean priest, the shaman, kahuna, or medicine man of today still uses exorcisms to drive out the evil spirits causing the maladies. The physician of today is thus a direct descendant of the Egyptian, Chaldean, and Druidic priests.

As man developed mentally, the supernatural elements gave way to factual truths, and history shows that the Greek natural philosophers founded the first era of what we might call modern medicine. Their works amply demonstrate that they were not influenced by gods, patriotism, or gain, but by truth for truth's sake. Thus, Protagoras, who so highly valued the mind, said: "I can know nothing concerning the gods, whether they exist or not, for we are prevented from gaining such knowledge not only by the obscurity of the thing itself, but by the brevity of human life." Concerning Protagoras, one can say that history preceded itself, for he was driven out of Athens as a reviler of the gods and his book was burned in the public market place. It was during this period, however, that the two great maxims which exerted so much influence on future thought came to light. The first was "Know thyself," which was inscribed in the temple at Delphi, wherein slaves and rulers sought guidance. It is attributed to Chilo, one of the Seven Sages of Greece, and we know that the maxim was considered by Socrates to be the only object worthy of man and the starting point of all philosophy. The second maxim, "Man is the measure of all things," which is as old as it is profound, was first uttered and stressed by Protagoras. One could proceed from the Ionian era and follow the various trends that led directly to modern psychotherapy. In a lecture on "The Freudian Epoch," [21] I chose to start with Spinoza, because this great thinker of the seventeenth century anticipated many of the truths that Freud later discovered and elaborated on the basis of clinical experience, and because it would have taken me too far afield to include everything before him.

You all know that the foundation for modern mental therapy was laid toward the end of the eighteenth century by the magnetist Mesmer, who received his diploma from the University of Vienna in 1766 for a thesis, "On the Influence of the Planets on the Human Body." The views he expressed show a mixture of physiology and astrology which was then in vogue. Later in-

[21] *The March of Medicine*, p. 68, Columbia University Press, 1943.

vestigators have claimed that these views were not original but that Mesmer absorbed them from Paracelsus and a Scottish physician, William Maxwell. There is no doubt, however, that Mesmer was a true pioneer who firmly believed in his discovery. After years of prosperity, during which he was acclaimed and idolized for his miraculous cures, he suffered shipwreck of his fortunes when he tried to gain recognition from the Royal Medical Society and from the Academy of Science of Paris. Neither the doctors nor the savants would have anything to do with him. It is of interest to note that Lavoisier and our own Benjamin Franklin were members of the committee of scientists and physicians appointed by King Louis XVI, in 1784, to investigate Mesmer's reputed cures. After a thorough investigation, the committee reported that the cures were genuine, but since they were altogether due to the imagination and imitation of the patients, the subject was not worthy of further scientific investigation. Mesmer died in obscurity about thirty years later, not dreaming that he had laid the foundations for hypnotism and suggestion and all the other forms of psychotherapy that started about a hundred years later.

There were many developments between 1784 and 1880 when Charcot began to pave the way for scientific psychotherapy, and some of them should be mentioned here. First, the Marquis de Puysegur discovered somnambulism. He found that some people could speak and act during the so-called magnetic sleep just as if they were awake, but that they retained no memory of their behavior. "They have acted," he said, "as if in a dream." Second, a Portuguese, Abbé Faria, demonstrated that some sensitive individuals are so impressionable that they could be put to sleep by a mere command that they should fall asleep. This showed that some people could be put to sleep without manual or magnetic contact, as Mesmer had always asserted. Finally, a number of English surgeons made use of the mesmeric technique in their practice and one of them, James Braid, concluded that there was no truth in Mesmer's "fluid theory," that the most important factor of this phenomenon was sleep, and he, therefore, called the whole procedure *hypnotism.* This, in brief, is the history of psychotherapy until the advent of Charcot and the other modern schools. What is most noteworthy in this whole history lies in the basic principle that one person could influence another person to the extent of curing him of disease. We know also that for centuries before this, it was universally accepted that one man could exert evil influence on another to the extent of killing him. All this was expressed in Mesmer's theory that human beings influence each other just as the magnet influences the iron—namely, that they either attract or repel each other. We must also bear in mind that the scientific committee which conceded that Mesmer's cures were genuine but were due "to imagination and imitation" made no effort to investigate the nature of the imagination and imitation that were responsible for these cures.

To return to our main theme, I wish to repeat that it had never occurred to me before I studied psychoanalysis that it was possible to obtain any information about a patient which transcended his own conscious knowledge. But after some experience with free associations and interpretation, I became convinced that the average person is as ignorant of the mental forces behind his thoughts and actions as is a traveler of the motive powers that propel the airplane, motorcar, or train that hurries him to some appointed place. All he wants is to reach his destination and he is entirely oblivious of the intricate forces of the machinery that actually carry him there. He is not interested in the science of dynamics, nor does he know whether the vehicle in which he happens to be is made of wood or steel, nor of the numerous complicated details that enter into its formation. Least of all does he think about the origin and evolution of the conveyance in question. As the human mental apparatus is infinitely more complicated than any machine made by man, we are justified in assuming that the average individual knows even less about the forces that impel his thoughts and actions than the putative traveler just mentioned. The obsessive patient whose case I described above (see p. 34) was treated in the Vanderbilt Clinic for some time before I became interested in him. As Dr. Clark who treated him did not know how to put into Greek the name of this obsessive tic, he thought that I might know and thus called my attention to the patient. The whole thing was Greek to him and would have been to me if I had not gone beyond the patient's conscious level.

Freud's psychoanalysis has been in existence for about two generations and as I myself have used it for thirty-seven years, I have no misgivings in calling it the microscope in the study of the mind. Through its use, psychiatry has taken on new meaning, new life. Instead of a restricted and circumscribed study of morbid mental behavior which it was when I first became a student of it, psychiatry is now a comprehensive science of both the normal and the abnormal phases of the mind, both of the individual and of the race. But to show how psychoanalysis wrought this change in psychiatry—a metamorphosis that is clear not only to me but is admitted even by those who are still more or less averse to Freud's views—it will be necessary to say something about Freud and the influences that guided him to his discovery.

Psychoanalysis was, practically speaking, a finished product when I first became acquainted with it. Indeed, I feel even now that anyone who can master the Freudian concepts that were known in 1908 will be a good interpretative psychiatrist. The Burghölzli library contained (the following works of Freud: *Studies in Hysteria*,[22] *The Psychopathology of Everyday Life*, *The Interpretation of Dreams*, *Three Contributions to the Theory of Sex*, *The Dora Case*, and *Wit and Its Relation to the Unconscious*.[23] These are still Freud's basic works and everything that he published later is only an elaboration and amplification of the theories expressed in them.) I therefore feel that any well-trained psychiatrist who is also well versed in these works will perforce practice good interpretative psychiatry. To be sure, he who wishes to qualify as a full-fledged psychoanalyst to treat complicated neuroses, such as hysterias and compulsive states, must go through a prolonged technical training as given in one of the institutes of the American Psychoanalytic Association. For there have been many accretions and modifications of the theories and practice of

[22] Written jointly with Joseph Breuer.
[23] All of these works with the exception of *The Dora Case* have been translated by me and published at different times.

psychoanalysis from 1907 to 1939. When Freud died at the age of eighty-three, he left twelve good-sized volumes and additional works, enough to fill at least two more volumes, for he was not a one-sided but a versatile genius whose interests reached far beyond the practice of medicine. One, therefore, need not know all of his works to be a proficient analyst. Thus in 1922 when I expressed to him my great admiration and enthusiasm after reading his book, *Das Ich und das Es* (The Ego and the Id), in which he first described the finer structures of the psychic apparatus, he said: "I am glad that you like it but one can be a first-class analyst without reading it."

What he demanded of a good analyst he clearly expressed in the following simple words which I have taken from his address given on the occasion of receiving the Goethe prize in Frankfurt in 1930. He said: "The set purpose of my life's work was to observe the finer disturbances of the psychic functions in healthy and sick people and to conclude or, better perhaps, to conjecture from such signs how the apparatus which controls these functions is constructed and what forces within it concur and conflict with each other." [24] These thoughts which specify the necessary qualifications for being a good analyst describe also the kernel of the neurosis which in a way resemble the thoughts quoted above from Adolf Meyer.

Of the works previously mentioned, *The Interpretation of Dreams* is Freud's major work and the one most difficult to master. In his foreword to its third English edition, Freud states: "It contains even according to my present judgment the most valuable of all the discoveries it has been my good fortune to make. Insight such as this falls to one's lot but once in a lifetime." [25] That the world of science has long ago confirmed Freud's judgment of this work is well known to most of you. Hence, from the beginning of the analytic movement, it was found best to study psychoanalysis through the analysis of one's own dreams. But this

[24] These words taken from his address were read by his daughter Anna, as he was too ill to attend the function.
[25] *The Interpretation of Dreams*, translated by A. A. Brill, New York, Macmillan Co., and London, Allen and Unwin, 1932.

is not always possible. The psychic forces underlying dreams are of such a resistive nature that even a trained objective observer is sure to overlook many elements, usually the most important ones of the dream. This was so well known in Burghölzli that when one wished to analyze his own dreams he usually asked someone who had already mastered the technique to control them with him. My own dreams were analyzed mostly by Jung, some by Bleuler, and later by Freud and Ferenczi. I had still other dreams which I analyzed myself following my return from abroad, later sending them to Freud with all the associations as well as with my interpretations. Invariably he pointed out many things that I had overlooked. As this occurred in every one of my dreams, despite the fact that I had already had considerable experience in both practice and theory, I became convinced that no one wants to look at himself as others do.

If one gives free associations to anyone who analyzes his dream, he opens up, as it were, his whole psyche—that is, if he really withholds nothing that flashes through his mind. Most of us were perfectly frank because we realized that this was the only way to learn the technique of analysis. It was also found that such mutual help in dream analysis turned out to be most successful if carried out by those who were in sympathy with each other, and that after a number of dreams had thus been analyzed, there developed a situation which in all respects resembled the present-day *lege artis* analysis. As a result of these experiences, the Zurich school was the first to advocate what is now officially designated as training analysis. There were some other factors that favored this development which I cannot discuss here; what I wish to stress is that present-day training analysis, which some psychiatrists still consider lightly, came into existence through long study and experience of seasoned psychiatrists.

Freud himself has repeatedly credited the Zurich school with the initiation of training analysis, and I am quoting him in confirmation solely because I want to give his reasons for advocating it as the best method of acquiring the psychoanalytic technique. His statement is as follows: "To the question how one can become an analyst, which I was asked years ago, I answered: through the analysis of one's own dreams. This preparation is surely sufficient for many persons, but not for all who would like to learn analysis. Nor are all those successful who wish to analyze their own dreams without outside help. I consider it as one of the many merits of the Zurich Analytic School that it emphasized this situation and made it a requisite that anyone who wished to analyze others should himself be analyzed first by an expert. He who is serious in this task should choose this road, which offers more than one advantage. The sacrifice to open oneself to a strange person without being compelled by sickness to do so is richly rewarded. Not only will one realize his wish to learn the hidden part of his own person in a much shorter time and with less emotional expenditure, but one will gain impressions and convictions about himself which he cannot obtain through the study of books and through listening to lectures. Finally the gain that accrues from the prolonged psychic relationship between the analysand and the analyst is not to be lightly estimated." [26]

Thus far I have, as it were, retraced my own steps from the time that I entered the psychiatric scene in New York until after I was accidentally transplanted into another country and what to me was a new psychiatric world. Carried away by my enthusiasm, I have perhaps anticipated myself and covered more ground than I wished on subjects that I should leave until later. It seems, however, that this is inevitable in such a presentation. Many ideas flash through the mind, but all of them cannot be reported because of the time that it would require and because of the unreasonable demand that it would make on your patience. I therefore ask that you bear with me a little longer while I add a few more impressions from Burghölzli.

In the hospital everything had to be *Alkoholfrei;* nothing alcoholic was consumed by us on the premises. We were all quasi-prohibitionists long before that noble experiment came to our shores. August Forel, who was Bleuler's predecessor in Burghölzli, and Emil Kraepelin were the foremost anti-alcoholic preachers in Europe. They carried on a vigorous propaganda against alcohol everywhere, in scientific and lay societies, all on purely scientific

[26] *Zentralbl. f. Psychoanal.,* II, 487.

grounds. Forel also started the anti-alcoholic movement in this country, but I was told that he severed his connection with the American movement when the church took possession of it. Bleuler was just as strongly against alcohol as Forel, so that none of the physicians drank anything alcoholic in the hospital.) We were not ordered to do so; the rule was self-imposed and we felt that we should stand as model examples for the nurses and attendants. This alcohol-free atmosphere contrasted sharply with my former state hospital environment where the old-timers, raging against the new order of 1902, were wont to seek refuge in large doses of C_2H_5OH from frequent note writing and other "newfangled Meyerian installations." As a reward for our voluntary abstention from alcohol, we received gratis as much nonalcoholic wine as we wished to drink.

Following my appointment, I was in charge of the male service where I worked harder than I ever had in all my life. If I did not wake up spontaneously, I was aroused at 6:00 A.M. by loud knockings on my door. Dressing and breakfast consumed half an hour and the morning rounds were made at 6:30. As I entered Ward I, I regularly met our director, Dr. Bleuler, already returning from his rounds. Following the rounds, we had staff meetings that lasted until about 10:30 A.M. After this, we had to dispense whatever medications we ordered for our patients. There was no pharmacist in Burghölzli in my time.

Perhaps my most pleasant memories of Burghölzli center about the informal late-afternoon discussions in the main office which, to use a popular expression, "were unprepared and unrehearsed." We would be through with our daily routine and finishing a few things in the office when someone would start some discussion, usually not of a psychiatric nature, in which everybody joined. In the end, we would naturally defer to the *Herr Direktor* or to his active *Sekundararzt*. On only one occasion, as I recall, did the discussion become serious and argumentative. It concerned the pathology of dementia praecox. Jung was inclined to assume a psychogenetic background for the disease, while Bleuler, though always stressing the psychological factors, nevertheless maintained that dementia praecox was physiogenic. This problem, which is still *sub judice*, seemed so much simpler in 1907. All the other discussions that I recall revolved around cultural problems such as the secret of music, fortune telling, and similar topics. It was on these occasions that Bleuler so well displayed his alert and brilliant mind. I always looked forward to these meetings and have often thought of them since.

The first lumbar puncture at Burghölzli was done by me and it took much persuasion before the *Herr Direktor* allowed me to do it. I had to assure him that I had learned the technique in Dr. Meyer's Institute and that I had done all the spinal taps in the Central Islip State Hospital for more than two years. Finally, after I had procured all the necessary implements for it, I performed the operation while the whole staff watched me. Fortunately, I had no difficulty in getting into the canal and obtaining the fluid.

Among our recreations I can mention the meetings of the psychoanalytic circle under the chairmanship of Dr. Jung. These meetings were well attended by many non-Freudian psychiatrists from nearby hospitals. As psychoanalysis was still new and the material presented was freely discussed, the meetings were, as a rule, very instructive and interesting, provided no one contradicted Freud's theories, for the chairman was at that time in no state of mind to tolerate such heresies.

One impressive episode that I recall vividly was a week-end visit from Kraepelin who, I was told, was in the habit of coming to Burghölzli from time to time. Youth does not, as a rule, entertain a high regard for its teachers but the respect, nay, reverence, in which Kraepelin was held by the younger generation of psychiatrists was touching and certainly well deserved.

Regular meetings were also held in von Monakow's clinic, I believe, every month, where besides neurology there were papers and discussions on such scientific subjects as optics. Dr. von Monakow was an interesting speaker, usually quite genial, but once he took a certain attitude he never swerved from it.

TWO

BREUER'S CATHARTIC METHOD THE PRECURSOR OF PSYCHOANALYSIS

MY FIRST visit to Freud was during the Christmas and New Year holidays of 1907–8. As we had been corresponding for some time, we knew each other fairly well by the time we met. It was then that we arranged that I should be his English translator, a work to which I devoted almost all my spare time for a period of more than ten years. It was also then that I visited Dr. Joseph Breuer whose permission I had to obtain for the translation of the first chapter of the *Selected Papers on Hysteria,* which Freud and I decided should form his first English book.[1]

In my eagerness to reproduce the psychiatric scene at the beginning of this century, I have reported what surged through my mind in as orderly a fashion as possible under the circumstances. I fear, however, that I have not fully succeeded. I know that I have left many gaps in some of the topics that I have passed over rather cursorily. As I have discussed these subjects so frequently over many decades, it has not been easy to follow a straight line without deviating to the right and left. But I feel that I have covered the roughest part of my road and that I shall now be able not only to fill the breaches but to advance more directly to my destination.

Freud was thirty-seven years old when in 1893 Breuer and he published a preliminary communication on "The Psychic Mechanisms of Hysterical Phenomena" in the *Neurologisches Centralblatt.* Two years later, in 1895, this paper was reprinted as the first chapter of the *Studies in Hysteria.*[2] This work is the *fons et origo* of psychoanalysis—indeed, of everything that was later formulated by Freud. It forms the keystone that unites the hypnotherapy of the end of the last century with the new psychotherapy

[1] *Selected Papers on Hysteria and Other Psychoneuroses,* Monograph Series.
[2] Translated by A. A. Brill.

of this century. There were many forces contributing to its formation, chief of which was Freud himself. But in order to understand
how psychoanalysis developed from the *Studies in Hysteria*, it will
be well to learn more about the man who was responsible not only
for its genesis but for laying the foundation for a new and most
revolutionary system of psychotherapy.

Freud was born on May 6, 1856 of Austrian Jewish stock and
lived in Vienna from the age of four until 1938 when he was forced
by the Nazi terror to emigrate to London where he died in 1939.
Much has been written about Freud's attitude to religion, some of
which is true and some misconceptions. In his autobiography, he
has this to say on the subject: "My parents were Jews and I
remained a Jew." In a letter dated February 26, 1925,[3] he stated:
"I can say that I am as little an adherent of the Jewish religion as of
any other religion, i.e., I consider them all most important as
objects of scientific interest, but I do not share the emotional feeling that goes with them. On the other hand, I have always had a
strong feeling of kinship with my race and have also nurtured the
same in my children." As a physician's religious belief has nothing
to do with his function as a healer, be he surgeon or psychiatrist,
Freud's attitude to religion should be of no greater concern to
the world than that of any other scientist.

Concerning his preparation for his scientific career, we can say
that Freud was always a brilliant student. While in college, his
record was so good that he was rarely required to take the regular
examinations. It is interesting to note that despite his brilliancy it
took him eight years, from 1873 to 1881, to obtain his medical
diploma. This was entirely due to the fact that he was in no hurry
to graduate. He seemed to have been more interested in the acquisition of knowledge than in the practice of medicine. That he
was able to follow so leisurely the plans he laid out for himself was
due to his father, who though a man in straitened circumstances
nevertheless permitted his son to choose his own vocation and
follow it in his own way. Freud tells us that he had no particular
love for the profession of medicine, neither in his youth nor later.
It seems that his curiosity was attracted more to human relation-

[3] Written to the editor of the *Jüdische Presszentrale* in Zurich.

ships than to objects of nature. Later in life, he once expressed the view that an early absorption in Biblical history at an age when he could hardly read had definitely determined the range of his later interest. Under the strong influence of an older college mate, he thought seriously of becoming a lawyer and then occupying himself with social problems. On the other hand, he was just then deeply impressed by Darwin's theories because, as he said, they gave promise of extraordinary progress in knowledge of the world. He adds: "I know that the lecture on Goethe's beautiful essay 'Nature,' by Professor Carl Brühl, delivered shortly before my graduation from college, decided me to matriculate in the medical school." [4] Anyone who reads Goethe's paean to nature will readily understand how the sensitive seventeen-year-old Freud felt at that time.

I have purposely presented this part of Freud's biography because it throws some light on his future attitude toward medicine. From what we can learn of his activities as a medical student, he seems to have devoted most of his time, about six years, to the study of the nervous system in Brücke's physiological laboratory. He admits that he was quite dilatory in his medical studies because, as he states, with the exception of psychiatry, the other medical specialties did not appeal to him. It was not until 1882, when he was admonished by the head of his department that the career of a theoretical researcher does not assure one of a livelihood, that he began to think seriously of medical practice. He then took his internship in the famous Allgemeine Krankenhaus (Vienna's General Hospital) and worked more than six months with Meynert, by whom, he states, he was fascinated while still a student. But faithful to Brücke, who originally assigned him to the study of the spinal cord of one of the lowest of fish, the *Amoecetes-Petromyzon*, he now went over to the central nervous system of man and devoted himself entirely to the medulla oblongata. He adds here that in contrast to the diffused nature of his studies during his first years in the university, he was now inclined to concentrate exclusively on one subject, on one problem.

In the light of what we have learned from Freud of child

[4] Freud: *Selbstdarstellung*, Leipzig, Meiner, 1925.

psychology, it is safe to assume that had he been forced in early life by his father to follow a strict curriculum, as is so often the case, he probably would have been incapable of persevering in the elaboration of his new and revolutionary theories, especially under the many difficulties he encountered. Speaking of his decision to confine himself to the practice of nervous diseases, he states that this specialty was only slightly developed in Vienna at that time. The neurological material was dispersed in the various medical divisions, hence the opportunities for studying it were poor. One had to be one's own teacher. But he added: "The great name of *Charcot* radiated in the distance."

However, in the years that followed, Freud worked hard and published a number of casuistic observations on organic diseases of the nervous system. He is proud of the fact that he was skilled in accurately localizing lesions in the medulla, and that he was the first in Vienna to send a case for post-mortem examination with the diagnosis of acute polyneuritis. As this was confirmed by autopsy, his reputation as a neurologist spread and thus attracted to him a number of American physicians to whom he lectured in a kind of pidgin English. But, he adds, since he knew nothing of the neuroses, his premature teaching activities came to an abrupt end one day after he had presented to his students a neurotic with localized headaches as a case of chronic circumscribed meningitis. His audience, he admits, justly revolted against this and left him. By way of apology, he adds that better people than he had at that time occasionally diagnosed neurasthenia as brain tumor. However, if one will take the pains to look over Freud's contributions to neurology, he will find an imposing list of works on clinical neurology, especially on hemiplegia, aphasia, and cerebral diplegia in children. Some of these works are still considered classics of modern neurology.[5]

Freud, as can be seen, had a good neurologic background, but he was not a trained psychiatrist. I have noted elsewhere that it was fortunate that he did not start as a psychiatrist because he might have become discouraged with the psychiatry of his time

[5] Smith Ely Jelliffe: "Freud as a Neurologist," *J. Nerv. and Ment. Dis.*, June, 1937.

and perhaps returned to his original intention of studying juris-prudence. That he made so many valuable contributions to psy-chiatry despite his lack of training in a mental hospital speaks for his great genius. Nevertheless, I have to admit that this lack of psychiatric training showed itself glaringly on some occasions. On the other hand, his well-founded neurologic background stood him in good stead whenever an occasion for such knowledge presented itself. I have elsewhere reported a case of chronic cephalalgia which was referred to me for analysis by Frederick Peterson. As the patient was about to attend to some business in Vienna, I sent him with a letter to Freud because I was not absolutely certain that he was a proper case for analytic treat-ment. Before the patient returned to this city, I received a letter from Freud in which he said that this was no case for analysis, that the patient suffered from "chronic internal hydrocephalus." We were all surprised to get such a diagnosis from Freud,[6] but to me the episode served ever after as an incentive for careful neurologic diagnosis. However, many years later when I read in his auto-biography that he had once lost his American students by diagnos-ing neurotic headaches as chronic meningitis, I wondered whether his careful diagnosis of the case of hydrocephalus was not un-consciously influenced by the trauma he had sustained at the beginning of his teaching career. When I called his attention to it, he smiled and said, "Very probably; we all learn from our former mistakes whether we know it or not."

Dr. Bernard Sachs, our grand old man of neurology,[7] worked side by side with Freud in Meynert's laboratory and had been my consistent and strongest opponent whenever I presented Freud's theories in his presence. But only a few years ago, while I was presiding at a joint meeting of the New York and Phila-delphia Neurological societies, Dr. Sachs took occasion to speak highly of me personally, although he repeated that he disagreed with my attitude toward psychoanalysis. I was naturally quite touched by Dr. Sachs's generosity and expressed myself to that

[6] A. A. Brill: "A Psychoanalyst Scans His Past," *J. Nerv. and Ment. Dis.,* May, 1942.
[7] Dr. Sachs died a few months after this lecture was delivered.

effect. As we left the meeting, Dr. Sachs turned to me and said: "I will tell you something that will surprise you," and he thereupon told me that he had recently received a letter from Freud in which Freud told him that he had never forgotten his neurology. Dr. Sachs was evidently very pleased to hear that. I was glad that the two distinguished old colleagues were again on terms of correspondence, but I was not surprised at what Dr. Sachs had just told me; it only confirmed what I had always known.

In recognition of Freud's contributions to neurology and histology, he was appointed a docent in neuropathology in the spring of 1885, and in the fall of the same year, at the recommendation of his former chief, Professor Brücke, he was granted a stipend to enable him to spend a year with Charcot. Speaking of this, Freud tells us that at first he was just one of many foreign students in the Salpêtrière of whom little notice was taken. Later, when he volunteered to put into German Charcot's "New Lectures," he was accepted into the inner circle and became one of the master's favorite pupils. I have learned independently that to be a translator of one's favorite author furnishes an open sesame to the latter's heart. But, to be sure, there is a psychological explanation for this situation into which we cannot enter here.

After about a year in the Salpêtrière, Freud returned home by way of Berlin where he stayed for a while in Baginsky's children's clinic. He was interested in children's diseases because he had been promised an appointment in the Department of Nervous Diseases for Children in Kassowitze's Institute in Vienna. This appointment, which he held for years, furnished the material for his works on one-sided and double-sided cerebral paralyses in children, published in 1897 in *Nothnagel's Textbook of General and Special Therapy*.

This is only a brief summary of Freud's preparation for his private practice which he began in the fall of 1886, following his marriage to Martha Bernays of Hamburg. It was by no means a one-sided training, as has been asserted by some of his opponents. Apropos of this view, I cannot resist giving the following interlude which he humorously relates in his autobiography. He states that his bride was to blame for his not having achieved fame in these early years. It seems that since 1884 he had been deeply interested in cocaine which was hardly known at that time. He obtained samples of this drug from Merck and studied its physiological effects. But in the midst of these experiments an opportunity presented itself to visit his fiancée whom he had not seen for two years. He therefore hurriedly finished his investigations and published a paper on the results of his experiments in which he predicted that this drug would soon be more widely used. Before leaving for his vacation, he asked his friend, the ophthalmologist Dr. L. Königstein, to determine to what extent the anesthetic effects of cocaine could be useful in ophthalmology. But when he returned from his vacation, Freud found that not Königstein but another friend, Carl Koller, whom he had also told about it, had made the experiments on animals and demonstrated his findings at the Ophthalmological Congress in Heidelberg. Thus, Koller is justly known as the discoverer of this local anesthetic which is now so important in minor surgery. Freud ends the story by saying that he bore no grudge against his bride for this loss of fame.

Although this story has no particular bearing on the main topic of our discussion, it throws some light on Freud's character. Far from being one-sided, he was, on the contrary, most well informed and versatile. There was hardly anything in nature that did not interest him. For example, during our walks in the Tyrolean Alps I learned much from him not only about the mind but also about mushrooms—so much about them, in fact, that I can now pick them in our woods and eat them with relish, to the great consternation of my family. That psychoanalysis has reached far beyond the confines of medicine is another indication of Freud's broad-mindedness.

Let us now inquire what influence hypnotism, which Freud studied seriously for the first time in the Salpêtrière, had exerted on the later development of psychoanalysis. Freud expressed himself very clearly on this point when he stated: "The importance of hypnotism for the genetic history of psychoanalysis cannot be easily overestimated. Both in respect to theory and therapy, psychoanalysis is the administrator of the estate which it has taken over from hypnotism." [8] What Freud means will be better understood later after we shall have learned more about Breuer and Freud's new concepts of hysteria.

Freud met Joseph Breuer in Brücke's laboratory, and although Breuer was fourteen years older and a busy general practitioner, there soon developed a close friendship between them. In their frequent discussions, Breuer once casually told Freud of a case of hysteria (the famous case of Anna O.) that he had treated from December, 1880, until July, 1882.[9] He told how the patient while in a hypnotic state once began to talk about the origin of her symptoms and went into its minutest details. What was most remarkable about this procedure was the fact that if she told everything that was connected with a symptom and at the same time gave free vent to the feelings that were originally expressed with the episode, the symptom then disappeared. As we shall all observe later, Freud was deeply impressed by what he heard, and thought of it often while studying with Charcot. In Paris he witnessed for the first time what one can really do with hypnosis therapeutically and experimentally. Freud has repeatedly recorded his experiences in the Salpêtrière and anyone who followed his later career could not fail to see the profound influence that Charcot had exerted on his later activities. Freud himself stressed the following facts that he carried away from the Salpêtrière: First, that Charcot could remove or produce hysterical symptoms through hypnosis. Secondly, that hysteria was found in both sexes, that it was not confined solely to the female sex. And last, but not least, that hysteria was a real morbid entity and not just a product of simulation, as had hitherto been believed. These facts must be borne in mind if one is to understand the later developments of Freud's scientific achievements.

When Freud returned to Vienna and made the first attempt to present these new views to the Vienna Medical Society, he was sorely hit by the reception he received. Thus, when he said that

[8] *Psychoanalysis: Exploring the Hidden Mysteries of the Mind*, translated by Brill, Encyclopedia Britannica, 1924.
[9] *Studies in Hysteria*, translated by Brill.

he was now convinced that hysteria could also afflict men, the chairman of the society said that this was incredible, and Meynert, his former professor and admirer, requested him to find such cases in Vienna and present them before the society. Freud then tells of the obstacles that were put in his way when he attempted to do so. The physicians in charge of the medical divisions refused to co-operate with him and one of them exclaimed: "But my dear colleague, how can you talk such nonsense! Hysteria really means uterus; how then can a man become hysterical?" He finally found, outside the hospital, a male patient presenting the classical signs of an hysterical hemianesthesia and presented him to the medical society.

"This time," he stated, "I was applauded, but no further interest was shown in me. The impression that the great authorities had rejected my new findings remained unshaken." He goes on to say that as a result of demonstrating male hysteria and the suggestive production of hysterical paralysis, he was "forced into the opposition." For very soon after this meeting he was excluded from Meynert's laboratory where anatomy of the brain was studied and throughout the whole semester he was unable to obtain a room for his lectures. This kind of treatment compelled him to withdraw from the medical societies which, he stated, he had not visited for a generation.[10]

Freud's reaction to those experiences may seem rather vehement and some even felt justified in suspecting that there was something neurotic about this behavior. But one who judges an emotional reaction not only by the present situation but also by the unconscious past, that is, if one defines a "complex" as "a past repressed emotional experience" and knows that it is dynamic and displaceable to anything that may touch it by some association—such a person must consider Freud's reaction as logical. This can be explained by the following episode: When Freud matriculated in the university in 1873, he tells us that he was shocked at the suggestion that he was considered inferior and nationally foreign because he was a Jew. He states: "I rejected the former with all the resoluteness at my command. I could never grasp why I should

10 *Selbstdarstellung*, p. 17.

be ashamed of my descent, or as they began to say 'race.' But as to national fellowship which was withheld from me, I renounced this without much regret. I felt that a zealous coworker will surely find a small place within the frame of humanity, without the necessity of such enrollment." But he goes on to say, "These first university experiences left an important impression on my future. I learned early that it was my lot to be on the side of the opposition, to be excommunicated from the compact majority." [11] Freud felt the effects of anti-Semitism throughout his life and repeatedly mentioned it in his writings. But it was this psychic trauma, this extratribal complex which he sustained at his entrance to the university, that unconsciously fortified the present shock of being excluded by his colleagues and, as it were, forced him again into the side of opposition because he brought Charcot's views to Vienna. When his new theories on the neuroses and sex came to light later, he encountered even more violent opposition, especially from Vienna colleagues, and the vague surmise felt by the boy of seventeen that it was his lot to be on the side of the opposition and be excommunicated from the compact majority then became a stern reality to the man of forty.

That he did not lose his reason shows that Freud was far from being a neurotic. He recounts that when he was with Charcot, he and the other *élèves* sometimes objected to the master's new and strange views. Charcot, he tells us, always settled such doubts in a friendly, patient, yet very firm manner, by repeating: "*Ça n'empêche pas d'exister.*" These words, Freud tells us, remained indelibly impressed on his mind, and I have no doubt that they often occurred to him when he was later assailed by violent opposition.

Lest I should anticipate much of my story, I shall now return to 1893 and relate how it happened that Breuer and Freud decided to publish their preliminary communications on their new theories of hysteria. When Freud entered private practice, he naturally wished to do something for his patients, but his entire therapeutic equipment consisted of two weapons, hypnosis and electrotherapy.

[11] *Ibid.*, p. 8.

There was also hydrotherapy, but to send the patient away to a hydrotherapeutic institute after the first examination offered a very scant livelihood. He recounts how he became engrossed in Erb's textbook on electrotherapy and followed its recommendations in every detail, but unfortunately the treatments did not help the patients. Long before Moebius uttered the redeeming words that the success, if any, of electrotherapy in nervous patients was due to suggestion, Freud had discarded the electrical apparatus.

Things, however, went better with hypnosis, of the genuineness of which he had been convinced since his student days when he witnessed a public performance by the "Magnetiseur" Hansen. Soon thereafter, Haidenhain took up the scientific cause of hypnosis, but for a long time to come the rank and file of the professors of psychiatry considered it fraudulent and dangerous, and any physician who dared interest himself in it was looked upon with suspicion and distrust. In Paris, however, he saw that hypnosis had been definitely accepted as a legitimate therapeutic method, and he himself witnessed the successful results of it. He also learned of the Nancy School which successfully utilized suggestion, with or without hypnotism. It was thus quite natural that during the first years of his private practice Freud should have relied mainly on hypnotic suggestion in the treatment of his patients. "The work with hypnosis was really seductive, and the reputation of being a miracle worker was very flattering," he states. He was still not long enough in practice to realize the shortcomings of this method. For the present, however, he complained only of two things: first, that not all patients could be hypnotized and, second, that some patients could not be put into a sufficiently deep sleep to produce somnambulism with amnesia, which he thought was indispensable for permanent cures.

To improve his hypnotic technique, he spent many weeks in Nancy during the summer of 1889. There he watched old Liébeault at work with poor women and children of the working classes, and witnessed also Bernheim's astounding experiments with hospital cases. He states that he became deeply impressed with the "possibility that there are mighty psychic forces which are still hidden from human consciousness." He also related how he persuaded one of his patients to follow him to Nancy for a consultation with Bernheim. She was a prominent and wealthy hysterical woman who had been sent to him for treatment because no one else could do anything for her. By hypnotic suggestion, he was always able to take her out of her misery, but she invariably suffered relapses. As he attributed these setbacks to his inability to put her into deep hypnosis with somnabulism and amnesia, he wished to learn from Bernheim how to achieve this. But after repeated attempts, Bernheim could do no more with her than Freud. Bernheim then frankly admitted that his striking therapeutic results with hypnotic suggestion were obtained only in hospital patients, and not in private practice. As a result of these experiences, Freud was now convinced that his inability to hypnotize some patients was due not to his faulty technique but to the obvious fact that *some people cannot be hypnotized.*

But Freud had never forgotten Breuer's case of Anna O. Once he even started to tell Charcot about it, but the latter did not seem interested. However, after he began private practice and nearly always used hypnotism in the treatment of his patients, it was only natural that he should have questioned them about the origin of their symptoms. For he soon found that such investigation in the waking state brought very meager results. Some patients vaguely remembered how the symptom began, while others knew nothing about it. In time, he felt that Breuer's method was not only more interesting but more efficacious than the mere commands or prohibitions which he imparted in ordinary hypnotherapy. Moreover, this method of investigation also gratified his own sense of curiosity concerning the origin of the symptom. He spoke to Breuer about the Anna O. case soon after his return from Paris, learned more details about his technique and decided to test this procedure of hypnotizing and investigation in his own cases. After he had confirmed Breuer's findings over a period of years with many of his own cases, he suggested to Breuer that they jointly report their discoveries, to which the latter finally agreed. In their first preliminary paper they gave a general outline of their discoveries, while in their book which appeared two years later, they gave detailed reports of a number of cases, with theoretical discussions. Breuer is thus the spiritual father of this method and Freud, to whom it served only as a starting point for his later discoveries, has always given Breuer full credit for it.

To understand the evolution of psychoanalysis from Breuer's procedure, it will be necessary to give a very short résumé of the case history of Anna O. as Breuer has reported it.[12]

Anna O. was a young woman of twenty-one years who became ill in 1880 while nursing her sick father to whom she was deeply attached. Breuer describes her as having a "keen and intuitive intellect, a sensitiveness for poetry and fantasy, which was, however, controlled by a very strong and critical mind which made her completely unsuggestible. Only arguments, no assertions, had any influence on her." In describing her other characteristic traits, he states that "her moods always showed a tendency to excessive merriment or sadness which made her more or less temperamental, and that the sexual element in her make-up was astonishingly underdeveloped. The patient, whose life became as transparent to me as seldom happens in the case of one person to another, never experienced any love, and in the whole mass of hallucinations which characterized her disease, this element of her psychic life never appeared."

Briefly she presented the following peculiar symptoms: paraphasia, convergent strabismus, disturbances of hearing, paralyses, and numerous contractures. These symptoms were later aggravated by the death of her father, when she then also showed numerous psychic symptoms. She could not recognize people; all human beings appeared to her as wax figures; she was very negativistic and evinced hallucinatory phases during which instead of her mother tongue she spoke and understood only English which she had studied in school. Thus, when she read aloud from French or Italian, she translated it by sight into excellent English. The course of her symptoms ran as follows: Every afternoon she became somnolent and this gradually increased into a deep stupor or hypnotic state at sunset. The patient used the English word "clouds" to describe this state. In the evening she invariably

[12] *Studies in Hysteria*, p. 14.

emerged from her stupor and was very lucid, calm, and even cheerful, busying herself with drawing or writing. She then continued in this perfectly rational state until four in the morning when she usually fell asleep for a few hours. But the next morning on awakening she was again confused and harassed by hallucinations, and sometimes became quite violent.

Closer observation showed that after the afternoon stupor had lasted for about an hour, she became restless, tossed about in bed with her eyes closed, and uttered some meaningless words. It was soon found that these words referred to something, to some situation that coursed through her mind while hallucinating. These hallucinatory situations usually began with the repetition of the word "torment," which was naturally interpreted as meaning that the patient was tormented by something. If close attention was paid to what she said later it was usually possible to find what ran through her mind. In due time it was discovered that while in this confused state she went through stories that were always sad but, in some part, pretty. They were constructed on the style of Andersen's *Picture Book without Pictures*. The beginning and the central point of the situation dealt mostly with a girl sitting, full of anxiety, near a patient. She always woke up calmly as soon as she finished the story and said that she felt "comfy" (comfortable).

As this course of events repeated itself regularly for many months, Breuer decided to turn it into a therapeutic technique. He then visited her every evening when he knew that she was in a state of hypnosis and "took away from her the whole supply of fantasms which she had collected since my visit." It was not always easy to induce her to express herself; sometimes she was irritable and refused to talk. On such occasions Breuer had "to extort it from her through urging and begging as well as through some tricks, such as reciting to her a stereotyped introductory formula of her stories." The patient called this daily therapeutic procedure the "talking cure" and humorously referred to it as "chimney sweeping." It was, as one can imagine, a very slow process and Breuer could not shorten it. He states that when he tried to shorten it by urging her to tell him directly the origin of a symptom, she invariably became confused, and her associations became considerably slower than when she was permitted to "wind off" slowly backward the thread of her memory.

Both patient and physician soon realized the tasks each had to perform. Breuer visited her every morning, hypnotized her by the usual procedure, and asked her to concentrate her thoughts on the symptom to which she had just reacted in order to find the causes that gave origin to it. She then described in rapid, short phrases all the external causes, which Breuer wrote down. In the evening hypnosis, she related in detail all the events of the series he had previously noted. All this was done with exhaustive thoroughness. As an example, he tells that for her symptom of transient deafness, she reproduced 108 detailed episodes, mentioning persons, circumstances, and also dates. The first person whom she did not hear as he entered was her father.

A quarrel in which she suppressed the answer caused a contracture of the glottis which repeated itself on every similar occasion for a long time.

The cough which was a frequent symptom throughout her illness appeared first while she kept a vigil at her father's bed and heard dance music coming from a neighboring house. She conceived a wish to be there which was immediately followed by self-reproach. Following this, she always reacted with a nervous cough whenever she heard music. It was by this slow, patient process that symptom after symptom was worked off until the whole hysteria came to an end.

Let us now see what Breuer and Freud concluded from this and other similar cases reported in their book on hysteria. Freud, summarizing the Anna O. case, repeats that in her waking state she knew no more about the origin of her symptoms than other patients, but that under hypnosis she always found the connecting links. All her symptoms were traced back to emotional experiences while nursing her father, and in this connection they were intelligible as remnants or reminiscences of affective situations. The individual symptom was not, however, a precipitate of one single "traumatic" scene but the result of a summation of many similar scenes. If the patient hallucinatorily recalled these situations under hypnosis and relived, as it were, the psychic act which she had formerly suppressed with all the feelings that originally accompanied it, the symptom disappeared.

The theories presented in the *Studies in Hysteria* were, according to Freud, quite unassuming; they did not go beyond the immediate expression of mere observations. The authors did not aim to fathom the nature of hysteria, but only to throw some light on the origin of its symptoms. They called their treatment the "cathartic method" because they thought that its efficacy was based on the mental and emotional purging—"catharsis'"—which the patient went through during the treatment. Hysteria, they said, was a disease of the patient's past. As Freud expressed it later, the symptom was, as it were, a monument of some disagreeable and forgotten (repressed) act of the patient's life.[13] The patient did not, however, recognize the significance of this monument any more than the average foreigner would understand the meaning of the Bunker Hill monument.

This concept for the first time showed the importance of distinguishing between conscious and unconscious mental states, and was later amplified and developed by Freud as the psychology of the unconscious. New meaning was also given to the affective or the emotional factors of life, its fluctuating course and dynamism, for the symptom was conceived as the result of a dammed-up or strangulated affect. The patient was unable to give expression to his feelings because the situation in question precluded it, so that the idea was *repressed* from consciousness and thus excluded from further elaboration. But as the repressed material remained dynamic and continuously strove to come to consciousness, the sum of energy finally worked itself to the surface on a wrong path to some bodily innervation and thus produced the symptom. In other words, the symptom represented a *conversion* of psychic energy into a physical manifestation, such as pain or paralysis, or into such an obsession as described above. Thus some neuralgic pain may have nothing to do with any disease of the trifacial nerve, but it may unconsciously signify: "I feel as if he had slapped me in the face." Since there could be no retaliation to this insult, the strangu-

[13] *Am. J. Psychol.*, 1910.

lated energy was repressed and gave rise to a feeling that resembled an organic neuralgia. The cure, or the mental and emotional catharsis, was effected through what the authors designated as the process of *abreaction;* that is, the hypnotized patient abreacted or worked off the repressed material by living through it and giving free vent in speech and action to the feelings that were originally excluded from consciousness. This process is not unlike similar situations in daily life. Aristotle expressed the same view when he stated the function of the drama to be a mental catharsis.

Let me illustrate this process of abreaction by a case that I reported long ago.[14] Years before the first World War, the New York press reported that there was a great need for laborers for the upstate harvest. Many tailors, shopkeepers and people in similar trades who were then out of employment were glad to take advantage of the opportunity, particularly since they heard that the pay would be quite substantial. When one of these men was put to work as a farmer, it was found that he was ill fitted or not strong enough for such work. The result was that he was made a fool of by the other farm hands. Being a sensitive person, he became quite sullen and morose, and when once, with provocation, he dared retort, he was given a sound thrashing and fired. What was more, the farmer refused to pay him what he thought was due him. As he could obtain no redress from the local court of justice and as he had not enough money to pay his return fare to the city, he was compelled to walk more than a hundred miles before he reached New York. When he returned, fagged out and starved, he cried for revenge. But when he consulted a lawyer, the latter asked for a retainer which he could not give. He was at a loss; wherever he turned he was frustrated. Obsessed with the injustice meted out to him, he talked about it continuously to his wife who did not give him much sympathy. Following such a discussion, when his wife told him to give up the idea of getting redress and look for work, he suddenly became fearfully excited. He shouted, kicked at the furniture, tore the pillows, heaping all the while all manner of abuse on the farmer. His wife had to call the police who

[14] Brill: *Fundamental Conceptions of Psychoanalysis,* p. 38, New York, Harcourt, Brace and Co.

took him to the Psychiatric Department of Bellevue Hospital where I saw him. I soon found that in his hallucination he continually raged against the farmer who he imagined to be right there before him. However, in a few days the patient became quiet and talked quite freely about his behavior which he now recognized as abnormal. As I grasped the true nature of the situation, I gave him every opportunity to unburden himself and he succeeded so well that he was discharged from the hospital within a few days.

I do not know what happened to this man later, but it is my surmise that he probably fared as well as ever. Had he repressed his feelings, he probably would have developed a chronic neurosis. As it was, he went through what we call a reactive manic attack and with the help he received later, he dissipated the surplus sum of energy which was produced by the insults and injustice which his organism could not assimilate.

THREE

THE SEXUAL ETIOLOGY OF THE NEUROSES

Not long after the appearance of the *Studies in Hysteria*, Breuer withdrew from his collaboration with Freud. There were many reasons for this step, but the foremost was the fact that he was then a man of about forty-five years who had hitherto enjoyed a lucrative practice as a family physician and a high reputation as a scientist. He was a pupil of Ewald Hering, the great physiologist, and his former scientific achievements were in no way related to the nervous and mental sciences. True, he had accidentally discovered the cathartic method in his effort to cure an hysterical girl, but, as noted before, he did not realize the importance of his discovery, and if he had not casually mentioned it to Freud, the whole matter would have been forgotten. Moreover, from the beginning of their collaboration, they differed in their explanations of the origin of pathogenic ideas. Breuer, influenced mainly by physiology, maintained that the repressed ideas originated in "hypnoid states." Freud, on the other hand, considered the pathogenic ideas as manifestations of strivings analogous to normal life. To him, the psychic splitting at the basis of the pathogenic ideas was the result of a repelling force which he designated as "defense."

Freud's view may have seemed less scientific than Breuer's, but it was more dynamic and in accord with situations encountered in everyday life. Here we may add that from the onset of his scientific development Freud showed this tendency to adhere to the simple and obvious situations of life. It was, to him, merely a question of following the circuitous paths that the neurotic was forced to take in his desperate effort to find his way in life, and no matter how labyrinthine they appeared, they always led back to the so-called normal starting point. That is how Freud demonstrated for the first time that there was really no gap between the seemingly most abnormal and normal manifestations of life.

On the other hand, being unprepared for new ventures, Breuer could not assimilate the new situations that suddenly confronted him. Soon after the book appeared he became discouraged by the welter of criticism the new concepts aroused in the conservative professors. Indeed, many of them began to rage as soon as they saw the introduction and never read the contents of the book. For in the introduction Breuer and Freud said that in the presentation of the new case histories they had to be guided by caution as much as by scientific consideration. They explained that as their experience was obtained in private practice from educated and prominent people, it would be not only a breach of confidence to publish such information but also a danger lest the patient be recognized. *"It is for this reason,"* they said, *"that we can adduce only very incomplete evidence for our view that sexuality plays the principal part in the pathogenesis of hysteria."*

You will recall that Breuer found nothing of love or sex in his first case, but as he and Freud continued to study more cases, they also had to broaden their view of sex, and then they found what Freud said later when he was alone, namely, that no matter with what symptom one starts, one finally always comes to the sphere of sexual experiences.[1] As they touched upon an extremely taboo subject—sex—they raised a storm the like of which had not raged since Darwin published his great work on the origin of the species. When the eminent authorities rejected the *Studies in Hysteria,* Freud merely smiled at their misunderstandings, but Breuer became depressed over them. He finally withdrew from the field which he had reluctantly entered, leaving Freud to pursue his own course. But Breuer's cathartic method remained as the solid foundation upon which Freud gradually erected his psychoanalytic structure.

The first and most important change that Freud made in his technique soon after he was on his own was to give up hypnotism, concerning which he had had strong misgivings for some time. In taking this serious step, he was well aware of the advantages

[1] "Zur Aetiologie der Hysterie," *Wien. klin. Rundschau,* 1896.

hypnotism offered. For it was a rapid and efficient instrument whenever it could be used and it was the only method by which one could broaden consciousness for the purposes of investigation. That he nevertheless decided to give it up was due to a number of potent factors that counterbalanced the advantages. For one thing, it was unreliable; some could not be hypnotized. Moreover, he always was somewhat antagonized by the way it was administered to the patient. Thus, in speaking of his observations in Bernheim's clinic in the summer of 1899, he states: "But I can recall that even at that time I had a feeling of gloomy resentment against this tyranny of suggestion. When a patient turned out to be recalcitrant to the suggestions, he was shouted at: 'What are you doing? *Vous vous contra-suggestionez!*' I felt then and there that such treatment savored of injustice and violence." [2]

But as hypnotism was absolutely indispensable for the cathartic treatment, many a worthy but unhypnotizable patient had to be given up. Freud was also dissatisfied with the therapeutic results of catharsis which were based on hypnotism. For although the results were sometimes very striking, they were often short-lived; those who were hypnotizable invariably suffered setbacks after a short or longer period of comfort. And just as the first magical successes enhanced the reputation of the therapist, the relapses equally served to diminish his prestige. I have known patients whom I would designate as hypnotism addicts. They could not go anywhere without the assurance that they would be near a hypnotist. Freud finally discovered that the best results of hypnotherapy depended mainly on the personal relation between the patient and physician. Hence if this subtle and friendly relation was disturbed, usually through no particular fault of the physician, the best results were immediately as if wiped out. To be sure, if there was a reconciliation, the patient felt well again but, says Freud, "This only demonstrated that the personal affective relationship was mightier than all the cathartic work, and just that factor was beyond control." [3] He then proceeds to recount an experience which showed him most glaringly what he had long suspected. One

[2] Freud: *Massenpsychologie und Ich-Analyse*, p. 40, 1921.
[3] *Selbstdarstellung*, p. 35.

of his most compliant patients, whom he had been able to free from attacks of severe pain by hypnotic therapy, once threw her arms around his neck as she awakened from her hypnotic sleep. The unexpected entrance of a servant saved them from a painful discussion, but they tacitly agreed to discontinue henceforth the hypnotic therapy. Freud adds that he then understood the nature of the mystical element that was behind hypnotism, and in order to eliminate it, or at least to isolate it, he had to give it up.

There was one experiment he witnessed in Bernheim's clinic that later helped him to span the gap formed by giving up hypnotism. The object of the experiment was to overcome the posthypnotic amnesia in patients who received suggestions while they were asleep. Ordinarily, the patients on awakening remembered nothing of what had transpired during the hypnosis; but in the experiment Bernheim insisted that they did know what happened, and requested them to recall it. He reiterated that all they had to do was to tell it, and at the same time laid his hand on their foreheads. After such repeated assurances, the forgotten memories actually returned, at first hesitatingly, and then in a stream with full clearness.

Freud decided to do the same when he gave up hypnotism. He reasoned that his patients must "know" everything that is accessible to them in hypnosis, and by assuring and urging, supported occasionally by pressure on the patient's forehead with his hand, the forgotten facts and connections finally came to consciousness. This was, to be sure, more laborious than placing the patient under hypnosis "but it was perhaps more instructive." He was thus able to dispense with hypnosis, retaining only the position of the patient on a couch, behind the head of which he sat so that he could see the patient but the patient could not see him. For a short time, he continued to use hand pressure to assist the patient, but that, too, was soon given up.

The patients were merely asked to tell everything that occurred to them, regardless of whether they considered it relevant or not. Above all, Freud admonished them to dispense with all criticism, to give up all conscious reflection, to abandon themselves to calm concentration, and to follow their spontaneous mental occurrences and then impart everything to him. In this way he finally obtained what he called "free associations" which gradually but invariably led to the origin of the symptom. As he gained more experience with this method, he found that it was not so simple as he had thought, that these so-called free associations were really not *free* but were determined by unconscious material that had to be analyzed and interpreted. This method Freud then designated as *psychoanalysis*. The cathartic method was thus preserved as the nucleus of psychoanalysis.

As Freud continued to delve into the mind by means of free associations, he gradually acquired an increasing insight into the mainsprings of human thought and action. The play of forces which were hidden by hypnosis slowly but surely revealed themselves. Thus, for some time he had wondered why the patients who had forgotten so much of their outer and inner experiences could nevertheless recall them by means of free association. The answer that finally obtruded itself was that the whole forgotten material was invariably of a painful nature. Its content was either terrifying or distressing or humiliating to the patient's personality. It was for that very reason that he forgot it, or, better, that he did not retain it consciously. It then became quite evident that to bring back to consciousness something that was strongly resisted by the patient, the latter's resistance must be overpowered first. The amount of effort the physician had to exert to bring this about depended on the particular case, and the force he expended in the procedure was obviously the measure of the patient's *resistance*.[4]

Having learned the meaning of the psychic processes of forgetting and resistance, Freud then reconstructed the pathogenic process as follows: If a craving of some sort comes into being in normal life and is forcibly opposed by another force, a psychic conflict ensues between the impulse and the resistance against it. The struggle then continues quite consciously for a while, until the impulse is rejected and its cathexis (the sum of energy) withdrawn from its striving. This, he said, represents the normal mode of adjustment. In the neurosis, the conflict comes to a different conclusion. Here the ego retreats from the unpleasant impulse at its

[4] *Ibid.*, p. 38.

first encounter with it, and thus closes to it all access to consciousness as well as to direct motor discharge; but the impulse retains its full cathexis or its impulsive energy. This, he said, constitutes the process of *repression* which he considered a new concept formulated by him. "Nothing like it," he said, "was ever recognized in psychic life."

As there are still many misunderstandings about the meaning of repression and suppression, I wish to emphasize that the former is an unconscious while the latter is a conscious process. Thus, a man may be tempted to commit a dishonest act by not telling the truth about his income to the tax collector. If he finally decides to tell the truth, even after a long struggle, the emotional feeling he had generated during the struggle quickly disappears and he is none the worse for the experience. Usually he feels better for it. But let us take the case of an elderly man who while camping in the woods alone with his stepdaughter, whom he had brought up as his own child, suddenly perceived a sensuous feeling while she kissed him good night. The idea was so shocking to him that it was stopped *in statu nascendi*. He stifled the feeling while it was being born, while it was forcing itself into consciousness, and then knew nothing about it. But the repressed material did not remain dormant, and finally worked its way to the surface on wrong paths and then manifested itself as symptoms.

Be it noted, however, that it was not the repression that caused the symptoms but the failure of it. And as the whole process proceeded unconsciously, he gradually developed symptoms that lasted for years. He remembered nothing about the kissing episode until it was brought up by free associations during the analytic treatment. The resistance against its becoming conscious was so forceful that he alone would never have brought it to consciousness. On the other hand, if he had consciously struggled with the temptation, no matter how long, and then suppressed it, that is, thoroughly controlled it, he would not have become neurotic. Let me repeat that suppression is nothing but conscious control of one's impulses which every animal must continuously exert for its own good. On the other hand, repression is an unconscious process which, because of its obnoxious content, is pushed altogether away from consciousness, and so long as it remains dormant in the unconscious, nothing happens.

The process of repression actually is a primary defense mechanism comparable to an effort to fly away from something. In order to keep the disagreeable strivings from consciousness and motor discharge, the ego runs away from it, represses it. But in the neurotic, the repressed primitive impulses refuse to abide in the unconscious, and finally find paths over which the ego seems to have no control. They then settle on some organ or part of the body which, though ill suited for the object of the original cravings, nevertheless assumes importance in the patient's mind as something strange and annoying. This new situation, which originates by way of compromise, constitutes the symptom or symptoms. But once this intrusion is established, the unity of the ego is constantly disturbed by it, and the ego, therefore, strives to combat it in the same way as it did the original unacceptable impulses.

To illustrate these mechanisms, which are simpler than they sound in theory, let us consider the case of an hysterical young woman who was ardently courted by a young man for some months. Suddenly one evening he made an unsuccessful sexual assault upon her and then vanished, leaving her in a state of deep depression. Because of her reserved nature, she could not confide in anybody and thus air her pent-up feelings. After brooding over this thwarted love affair for some time, she began to show numerous symptoms of the conversion hysterical type and also had attacks that resembled epilepsy. These symptoms had existed for about two and a half years before I was consulted. Analysis showed that the symptoms and attacks were symbolic representations or dramatizations of what had taken place at the time of the abortive sexual assault. Every detail of the seemingly epileptiform attack—every movement, every gesture—represented a stereotyped repetition of the repressed sexual situation which the patient now reproduced unconsciously.

The whole process of this malady can readily be understood if we follow the various steps of the amour. The young woman was healthy and, biontically speaking, ready for mating; her natural sex instinct was striving for fulfillment. However, consciously, she could think of love only in the conventional morality sense of the term, in which the physical factors were deliberately kept out of sight. Her bourgeois, religious upbringing precluded any illicit sexual activity so far as her conscious thoughts were concerned. Yet behind it all, her feminine being was actively striving for maternity. She was sincerely enamored of the man, but she naturally thought of it in terms of love and marriage with everything that goes with them. The brutal shock of having the physical elements of sex suddenly thrust at her produced a frightful impression on her mind. On the one hand, she consciously rejected vehemently the lover's physical advances, and on the other hand, she unconsciously craved them. For weeks after the attack, she vividly lived over in her fantasy everything that had happened to her, and occasionally she even fancied herself as having yielded—a thought that was at once rejected and substituted by a feeling of reproach and disgust. Last, she missed the love making she had enjoyed during the months before the attempted assault. As she could not unburden herself to anyone, she strove hard to put everything out of her mind and finally succeeded in forgetting everything. But a few weeks later, she began to manifest the symptoms that finally developed into the pathogenic picture which was diagnosed as epilepsy or hysteroepilepsy. Analysis demonstrated that all her symptoms were disguised compromise formations of the whole affair, of the conflict between her primitive self and her ethical self, or, as Freud put it after he formulated the psychic apparatus, of a conflict between the ego and the id.[5]

Speaking of the great contrast that exists between hypnotic suggestion and analysis, Freud expressed it as follows: "In truth, the greatest possible contrast exists between the suggestive and the analytic technique, that contrast which the great Leonardo da Vinci has expressed for the arts in the formulae *per via de porre* and *per via di levare*." [6] He then goes on to say that the artist

[5] This case was taken from my introduction to *Freud's Basic Writings*, Modern Library, 1938.
[6] *Selected Papers on Hysteria and Other Psychoneuroses*, p. 178, translated by A. A. Brill, Monograph Series, 1909.

works with the first formula; he puts little heaps of paint on the empty uncolored canvas, and in this way he produces the image that he, the artist, desires. On the other hand, the sculptor works by taking away; that is, he takes away from the stone as much as covers the surface of the statue contained therein. Similarly, suggestive therapy does not concern itself about the origin, force, or significance of the morbid picture; it strives only to put on something, the suggestive command through which it hopes to keep the pathogenic idea from expression. On the other hand, analytic therapy does not wish to put on anything; it does not wish to introduce anything new into the patient; it aims to take away, to extract, what was superimposed on the patient's personality. It is for this reason that analysis concerns itself with the origin of the symptom. I might add that, bearing this in mind, one can also understand why psychoanalysis is applicable only to persons who were born with a normal mentality and are of good character, while it makes no difference to whom hypnotic and suggestive commands and prohibitions are applied. The patient whom I have just described could not have been cured by hypnotic suggestion.

The description of this case history is not, however, to be considered a paradigm of a complete analysis of a case of hysteria as it would appear today. Here I have merely endeavored to show how we look at neurotic symptoms psychoanalytically, in contrast to the hypnotherapeutic and other psychotherapeutic methods. Anyone reading such a history is usually impressed with its simplicity. A number of people who have read it told me so, but I wish to inform them that it is more complicated than it seems. It is as if one were to look on a wedding ring as a mere gold-plated circle of metal without considering the past history of the physical and psychic evolution of the wedding ring: the time and effort required to extract the metal from the bowels of the earth, the time and skill it took to mold the metal into its present form and, finally, the psychic and emotional evolution of it as a symbol for the most difficult institution evolved by civilization. Yet even this scant description of the psychogenetic causes of the young woman's malady shows the role attributed by Freud to the unconscious factors of the mind. Psychoanalysis has been justly called by Bleuler "the psychology of the depth" since it is the only science that concerns itself mainly with the unconscious factors of the mind. Unlike the psychologists and philosophers who use such terms as conscious, coconscious, and subconscious in a very loose and vague manner, Freud has a definite scheme of the mental apparatus based on a large empirical material and confirmed for many decades by others. To Freud *consciousness* is merely an organ of perception. One is conscious or aware of those mental processes that hold his attention at any given time. In contrast to this, the *unconscious* is utterly unknown to him and cannot be voluntarily recalled. No one can bring to light anything that is repressed into the unconscious unless he is helped to recall it by hypnosis, or unless it is interpreted for him by psychoanalysis. Midway between the Freudian conscious and unconscious there is the *foreconscious* or *preconscious* which contains forgotten memories that can nevertheless be eventually recalled through the exertion of some effort.

These spatial divisions of a conscious, a foreconscious, and an actual unconscious were formulated by Freud in his attempt to conceive, theoretically of course, the psychic apparatus as a composition of a number of forces or systems. Theoretical as it is, it nevertheless works well in practice and, as will be shown later, "*the dream,*" as Freud puts it, "*is the via regia to the unconscious.*"

Most of the mechanisms underlying everyday slips in talking, reading, writing, misplacing, as well as the forgetting of names and other things that were once well known to the individual, are all based on some disturbance in the foreconscious. Freud devoted a most interesting work to these manifestations, *The Psychopathology of Everyday Life,*[7] after the free-association method convinced him that there was nothing arbitrary or accidental in normal or abnormal psychic activities. For the same manifestations of unconscious forces which he discovered at the basis of the neuroses were also found in the ordinary faulty actions of daily life. The difference, however, lies in the fact that the neurotic symptoms have their roots in the unconscious and consequently must be

[7] *The Basic Writings of Sigmund Freud,* p. 34.

analyzed to show their meaning, while the disturbances that give origin to the slips and faulty actions emanate from the fore-conscious and hence are usually understood by those making or hearing them. Thus, Prime Minister Winston Churchill in his address at Harvard University, on the occasion of receiving an honorary degree, touched off a ripple of laughter, according to the New York *Times*,[8] with a rare lapse in his famous oratory. "He sailed smoothly through his verbal transition of man, from the horse and buggy days to the day of the eagle—eagles being represented by the *infernal* combustion engine." He quickly corrected his words to "internal combustion engine" which amused him as much as his audience.

A little reflection can readily show the reason for this *lapsus linguae*. As the prime minister waxed oratorical on man's tremendous progress from the horse and buggy period to the height of eagles through the invention of the internal combustion engine, his thoughts must have been suddenly disturbed by the memories of the London and Coventry blitz destructions, by the ruthless annihilation of hundreds of innocent women and children which was made possible by just such *infernal* combustion engines. In other words, his euphoric mood, while orating on the great progress produced by the ingenuity of man's great inventions, was stopped short by the reminder that this invention works perhaps more havoc than benefit. In other words, he might have thought of what another great thinker, Goethe, expressed so long ago:

> Ein wenig besser würd' er leben,
> Hätt'st du ihm nicht den Schein des Himmelslicht gegeben;
> Er nennt's Vernunft und braucht's allein
> Nur tierischer als jedes Tier zu sein. (*Faust*)

(Man would have lived better if thou had'st not given him that gleam of heavenly light which he calls reason, which he uses only to be more animal than any animal.)

The most primitive warriors regularly spared women and innocent children, while bombs hurled from sky fortresses carried by internal combustion engines are no respecters of age or ca-

[8] September 7, 1943.

thedrals. Such thoughts must have flashed through the mind of Mr. Churchill when he made this slip of the tongue. His rapid flow of oratory suffered, as it were, a derailment through the collision of the antonyms "progress" and "retrogression." The result of this collision of foreconscious thoughts, the slip of the tongue, catapulted his audience into a mood that was far from the prime minister's intention. Instead of remaining spellbound by the seriousness of his speech, they suddenly responded with a ripple of laughter.

Incidents like this are often amusing, though sometimes also very embarrassing, but they clearly demonstrate the unconscious mental operations constantly at work in our speech and acts. In order to adjust himself to the demands of civilized life, the average person is constantly assailed from all directions by forces that he has to dodge, without at the same time stepping on his neighbors' toes. We are taught these tricks from the very beginning of our childhood and the average adult somehow manages to get along. At worst he makes a *faux pas* on some occasions which, by mutual agreement, we overlook. But the most bizarre neurotic or psychic formation is not different mechanically or psychically from the innocent slip I have just described.

FOUR

FREUD'S CLASSIFICATION OF THE NEUROSES

EVERYTHING I have presented so far emanated from the study of hysteria which fascinated Charcot and Freud in turn. It seems that hysteria was to the psychopathologists of that time as the transparent eggs of the sea urchin have always been to the biologist. But as Freud continued to practice, he naturally saw many neuroses that were not hysterias. However, as he had learned from his studies of hysteria that its etiologic factors were regularly of a sexual nature, either as actual sexual conflicts or as aftereffects of previous sexual experiences, he now turned his attention to the sexual life of a large group of patients who were known as neurasthenics. As soon as he started his investigation, he found that what was ordinarily called neurasthenia, in the original sense of George Miller Beard, was made up of a mass of cases that differed from one another in appearance, etiology, and mechanisms. After considerable study, Freud decided to separate from neurasthenia all cases of pathologic anxiety which he designated as "anxiety neurosis." Stekel later showed that most of these cases were really hysterias whose dominant symptom was anxiety.[1] In addition to the anxiety neurosis group, Freud also separated from neurasthenia all those cases that were falsely so diagnosed, such as mild dementia praecoxes, cyclothymic depressions, incipient pareses, latent phthisis, and other organic affections. After he had eliminated all these cases, neurasthenia became contracted into a very small entity which, according to Freud, was characterized by the following symptoms: headaches or pressure feelings in the head, spinal irritations, dyspepsia with flatulence and constipation. When he investigated the sexual life of these groups, he readily discovered that, as in hysteria and compulsion neuroses, these patients, too, showed a sexual etiology, but of a

[1] Stekel: *Nervöse Angstzustände,* Wien, 1908.

physical nature, such as coitus interruptus, frustrated excitement, sexual abstinence, excessive masturbation, and nocturnal pollutions. In explaining the *modus operandi* of these sexual abuses in the actual production of the symptoms of anxiety, Freud made good use of his neurologic knowledge,[2] which all who are interested might read in his own words. In brief, the *actual neuroses*—anxieties, neurasthenia and hypochondriasis—are due to real somatic sexual injuries of a chemical and toxic nature, or to the replacement of an adequate (action) discharge by a less adequate one, as normal coitus by masturbation or spontaneous pollutions, while the *psychoneuroses* or the *transference neuroses* are due to psychosexual traumas.

Having come to this conclusion, Freud said that *in a normal sexual life no neurosis is possible*, and he added: "My medical conscience felt satisfied with this formulation." It pleased him to find that sexuality was not merely a psychic matter, but that it also had a somatic side, that one could ascribe to it a special chemism, and that sexual excitement depended on the presence of some as yet unknown material. Freud then states that he had no opportunity for further investigation of the actual neuroses, nor was it taken up by others. "If I look back today," he wrote, "to my former results, I consider them as a first crude schematization of probably a far more complicated state of affairs."

Those who follow Freud's classifications of the neuroses often find that one can obtain gratifying results in the treatment of the actual neuroses with little effort, in contrast to the long and patient application that is required for similar results in the psychoneuroses. In many actual neuroses, all that one has to do is substitute an adequate for an inadequate outlet, such as a contraceptive for coitus interruptus or some instruction about the physiology or psychology of sex. But such cases are rare and they do not teach us anything in comparison to the transference neuroses that occupy most of our time. The latter represent the real borderline cases; they demand prolonged and laborious application for the livelihood they furnish us, but they are interesting and instructive. I

[2] *Selected Papers on Hysteria and Other Psychoneuroses*, ch. VI, Monograph Series.

have repeatedly heard some of my colleagues who practice other specialties ask, "Brill, how can you sit the whole day and listen to all these crazy things; aren't you afraid of getting nutty yourself?" My usual retort is, "If I were as disinterested in mental mechanisms as you are, I would have been long ago." Only recently, I was again asked this same question by a colleague to whom I had to give a bad prognosis about his psychotic daughter whom I had just examined. As he specializes in proctology, I was ready to give an adequate retort, when I was quickly restrained by the thought that the question that he put to me so jokingly really represented his own fears which he unconsciously projected to me.

There are still two more topics that I must briefly discuss before proceeding to Freud's direct contributions to the psychoses. The first is the subject of dreams, concerning the psychoanalytic importance of which I have already spoken. Dream interpretation was mentioned for the first time when Freud spoke of the need for more convincing evidence on certain new theories referring to the composition and the modes of operation of the psychic apparatus. He said: "In a work on the interpretation of dreams which I am now preparing, I shall have the opportunity to touch upon these fundamentals in the psychology of the neuroses." [3] Freud later called analysis a child of the twentieth century because *The Interpretation of Dreams*,[4] with which it was ushered into the world, first appeared in 1900. What Freud really wished to convey was that the structure of psychoanalysis was not complete until dream interpretation became a part of it. The first time he used the technique of dream interpretation was in the analysis of the Dora case [5] which he carried out in 1899. In the history of the psychoanalytic movement,[6] Freud states that while he and Breuer were collaborating, they endeavored to guide the patient's attention directly to the traumatic scene in which the symptoms

[3] *Wien. klin. Rundschau*, 1898, reprinted in the *Neurosenlehre*, 1st Series, p. 200.
[4] *Psychoanalysis: Exploring the Hidden Mysteries of the Mind*, translated by A. A. Brill, Encyclopedia Britannica, 1924.
[5] *Collected Papers*, vol. III, London.
[6] *The Basic Writings of Sigmund Freud*, p. 931, translated and edited by A. A. Brill, Modern Library.

had arisen, that it was there that they found the psychic conflict and thus freed the repressed affect. This procedure was so characteristic of the psychic processes of the neuroses that they designated it as *regression*. The patient's associations always went back from the scene to be explained to earlier experiences and thus forced the analyst to delve into the past.

At first this regression went regularly to the age of puberty; later, however, "such failures as gaps in the understanding tempted the analytic work further back into the years of childhood which had, hitherto, been inaccessible to every sort of investigation. This regressive direction became an important characteristic of the analysis." He goes on to say that it was a great temptation to stop short and that he sometimes yielded to it. But in the Dora case he knew the scene that caused the outbreak of the illness and no matter how often he tried to analyze directly this experience, he could obtain only the same scanty and broken descriptions. "Only after a long detour," he states, "which led through the earliest childhood of the patient, a dream appeared, in the analysis of which the hitherto forgotten details of the scene were remembered, and this made possible the understanding and solution of the actual conflict." It was, therefore, this experience that confirmed Freud's former belief that the dream must be treated as a symptom and that only through dream analysis can one penetrate into the earliest period of childhood.

Dream interpretation thus marks the beginning of child analysis which has since then developed into an important specialty. Indirectly it has influenced all students of child life, even those who do not claim to follow Freud. In other words, dream interpretation has not only completed the structure of psychoanalysis but it has also furnished the key to the infancy of the individual as well as to that of the race. To be sure, J. J. Rousseau in his *Émile* stressed the importance of the psychic life of the child and, consequently, the work was later burned in Paris. But systematic observation of child life was initiated by Freud and his school through the analysis of dreams. Thus, with the beginning of the twentieth century, the structure of Freud's psychoanalysis was completed. For through the use of free association and the art of interpretation, Freud discovered that the dream, like the neurotic symptom, was a compromise formation of a struggle between an impulse and a resistance against it.

The dream, according to Freud, represents a hidden fulfillment of an unconscious wish. But the wishes it represents, or strives to represent, as fulfilled are the very same unconscious wishes that are repressed in the waking state and then become neurotic symptoms. Dreaming is a normal function of the mind; it is the guardian of sleep in so far as it strives to relieve tensions generated by unattainable wishes—tensions which, if not removed, might prevent the person from sleeping. The dream does not always succeed in its efforts to guard against disturbances of sleep. Sometimes if it oversteps the limits of propriety, if it goes too far in its effort to realize some obnoxious wish, the dreamer is awakened by the higher forces within him, by his super or ideal ego.

Without going further into the psychology of the dream, we can say that unconscious psychic processes are active in every normal person, that they express themselves as inhibitions and other modifications of intentional acts, and that the dreams of persons who are mentally healthy are of the same construction as neurotic and psychotic symptoms. But as the dream is a phenomenon of normal psychic life, Freud concluded that psychoanalysis was not merely a new instrument for the investigation of psychopathology but also for the exploration of normal psychic processes.

A year later, in 1901, Freud published his interesting work, *The Psychopathology of Everyday Life,* and in 1905 his *Wit and Its Relation to the Unconscious,*[7] in which he demonstrates that one of the greatest social outlets of modern man, namely, wit, shows the same constructions as the dream and neurotic and psychotic symptoms. These works definitely wipe out the putative line of demarcation between normal and abnormal psychic expressions because they show that the same mental processes that are at the basis of hysterical symptoms, obsessions, phobias, hallucinations, and delusions are also found in faulty acts and other expressions of normal life. That this has been amply demonstrated

[7] These works form part of *Freud's Basic Writings.*

is shown by the fact that psychoanalytic literature abounds in studies that throw a new light on mythology, religion, folklore, and fairy tales, all of which represent the dreams of yesterday. In fine, psychoanalysis has become as important to the nonmedical sciences as to the study and treatment of the neuroses.

Most people who speak about Freud and psychoanalysis invariably think of sex and usually dot their remarks with something to the effect that Freud exaggerates the sexual factors in life or that he centers everything on sex. I have already shown how Freud came upon the role of sex in the neuroses, but I have not as yet said what Freud really means by sex. Let me, therefore, begin with a quotation from Dr. James J. Putnam, former Professor of Neurology at Harvard University: "Freud has made considerable addition to this stock of knowledge, but he has done also something of greater consequence than this. He has worked out with incredible penetration the part which the instinct plays in every phase of human life and in the development of human character, and has been able to establish on a firm footing the remarkable thesis that psychoneurotic illnesses never occur with a perfectly normal sexual life."

These words, taken from the introduction Dr. Putnam wrote in 1910 to my first translation of Freud's *Contributions to the Concept of Sex*,[8] are repeated here because I was extremely pleased to have the support of a highly respected New England scholar when I was about to bring this work before English-speaking readers. I have quoted this dictum above in Freud's own words and his remark that although the statement made him unpopular, it nevertheless satisfied his medical conscience. To say that the pronunciamento made him unpopular is to put it mildly indeed. As a matter of fact, it would be impossible to convey even a small degree of the vituperation, mockery, nay, persecution, which he consequently suffered for a great many years. Now and then, one still hears some echoes of it, but they are mere whispers in comparison to the vociferous ragings of the first decades of this century. For the European world was still under the spell of the church fathers who, with the advent of Christianity, had sternly

[8] *Three Contributions to the Theory of Sex*, in *Freud's Basic Writings*.

suppressed everything sexual simply because the pagans had dei-
fied sex, and as this suppression had continued for centuries, sex
was identified with sensuality, secretiveness, and disgust which
none dared face. It was not only his fellow psychiatrists who re-
viled Freud, but every incompetent who wished to see his name
in print. For no matter how utterly stupid, how absolutely untrue
such outpourings were, they always obtained a ready hearing in
the medical and lay press. Following my introduction of Freud's
works here, I was subjected to the same sort of treatment, but
having been forewarned by Freud himself, I was well prepared for
it. (It got so that when I heard such foolish or unfactual statements
at meetings, I challenged the speaker to tell where Freud said it
and offered $100 to any charity if the particular statement could
be found in Freud's works. As time went on, I became increasingly
bolder and I raised the stake to $500 and even more. This mode of
repartee I found to be most effective against the absurd fantasies
that were spun about Freud's ideas of sex.)

Yet anyone who had stopped to think could have readily seen
that Freud was not the first to discover sex or sexual difficulties in
man. The literature of our whole civilization contained an abundance of material on love or sex long before Freud became interested in the subject. Freud's special merit lies in the fact that
before him sex had been treated as an isolated phenomenon or as
(more or less) an abnormality, whereas he evaluated it as a component of the normal personality. Before 1900, only a few daring
spirits wrote about sex and as they mostly confined themselves to
the abnormal aspects of it, no one seemed to care; as a matter of
fact, only very few physicians knew the works of Havelock
Ellis or of the other sexologists. But when Breuer and Freud found
the important part that sex plays in normal and abnormal psychic
life, and when Freud later stated that no neurosis can develop in
a normal sexual life, sex was taken out of its narrow, obscure confines and brought, as it were, into every respectable home. For
neuroses were as prevalent at the close of the last and at the
beginning of this century as they are today; and as there was hardly
a person who did not have some neurotic person in his family, the
righteous anger this promulgation brought forth was quite natural.

However, as Freud became increasingly more interested in the sexual manifestations of patients, forced upon him by his psycho-analytic observations, he finally formulated his concepts in *Three Contributions to the Theory of Sex*, a knowledge of which I must presuppose on the reader's part. Freud maintained there that sex could not be restricted to the physical functions of mating, that sex was a primary instinct composed of many partial impulses serving various aims, and that every child brings along into the world the germs of sex which develop and take on new forms with age. But in attributing sex to every child and calling it "poly-morphous perverse," that is, perverse in all directions, Freud in-curred the displeasure of the world. It did not help him to explain that the reason the child has no sense of *sympathy, shame, modesty, disgust* or *morality*, all the great assets of civilization, is because he has not yet become adjusted to the restrictions that civilization imposes on every person during the first years of life. The very fact that he associated the child with sex, as the average man understood it at that time, was enough to arouse opposition to everything he said.

Freud repeatedly said that he considered sex in the broad sense of love, and that sex must be considered as any other instinctive activity in man. The neurotic symptom, as he had shown, was not something that just flew into the patient; on the contrary, it de-veloped slowly on the basis of a special constitution and fate, i.e., heredity and environment. He viewed the sexual life of man in the same light. Sex surely does not fly into the individual at puberty as some imagine. Puberty means maturity and maturity signifies a gradual development; as Cicero puts it: *"Omnia quae terra gignit maturata pubescunt."* The individual having reached a certain age is ready for reproduction and is under a compulsion to achieve it. It seems quite simple as we observe it in nature. There is, to be sure, a struggle to obtain the mate, but the fittest invariably attain this goal. In civilization, however, it may be quite different; boy meets girl and wishes to mate, but he encounters many ob-stacles to this natural or, one might say, divine law. Why? Because with the advance of civilization the individual's sexual activities had to be curbed. But as the method of curbing is still imperfect, many who are incapable of adjusting themselves to these restrictions deviate from the natural paths in one way or another.

Sexual abnormalities thus originate in the same way as physical anomalies, despite the fact that sexual disturbances have always been considered as peculiar phenomena that have no relation to normal sex. Such views are just as illogical as if we were to look upon a person who is suffering from the results of infantile paralysis as entirely unrelated to normal human beings. Nevertheless, given certain abnormal conditions, anybody can develop an inversion or perversion through no fault of his own, in the same way that he can contract typhoid or sleeping sickness. Freud was the first to demonstrate the causes of such abnormalities; in the same way that other scientists had demonstrated the causes of physical diseases. Briefly, Freud comprised all sexual functions in the term *libido,* which he defined as a quantitatively changeable and not yet measurable energy of the sexual instinct which is usually directed to an outside object. He explained that the sex instinct consisted of all those impulses that center about love in the broad sense, that its main component is sexual love, and sexual union is its aim; but that it also includes self-love, love for parents and children, friendship, attachments to concrete objects, and even devotions to abstract ideas.

Bearing in mind this broad concept of sex, let us now follow its paths in neurotic states as conceived by Freud. The homestead of the libido, he tells us, is in the ego, in which it is altogether centered during childhood. Freud designated this as *ego libido,* for the child is purely egoistic and up to the age of approximately four he lives an *auto-erotic* or self-gratifying existence. To be sure, he leans on the mother for his gratification of hunger and love in the form of protection, but he needs no other outlets from without, and he does not consider her as outside of himself. But as he grows older, he reaches what Freud called the *narcistic* state of development, i.e., he becomes more and more cognizant of himself as a being which absorbs all his interest. Freud speaks of this as *narcistic libido* because, unlike the pure ego libido, it is erotically tinged. Like Narcissus of the myth, the child is, as it were, in love with himself. However, as he grows older and successfully goes through the early phases of development, he is then able to transfer libido to objects outside of himself and we then speak of the stage of *object libido*. The latter reaches full development around the age of puberty when the organs of reproduction have attained maturity. Psychoanalysis shows, however, that under certain conditions object libido can be withdrawn back to the ego. Many normal and pathologic states depend on the resulting interchange between these two forces.

Thus, the so-called *transference neuroses*—hysteria and compulsion neuroses—result from disturbances in the give and take of object libido, and hence are, as a rule, amenable to psychoanalytic therapy; whereas the narcistic neuroses, or the psychoses, can be studied and helped but cannot be entirely cured by analytic therapy. The psychotic is, as a rule, inaccessible to treatment because he is incapable of transferring sufficient libido to establish the proper rapport with the therapist. By virtue of the delusions that control him, he is too suspicious or too absorbed in his own inner world to pay any attention to anybody else. There are many exceptions to this as every experienced analyst knows, but in general the libido disposition in the various neuroses is as described.

As will be shown, by broadening the term sex into love or libido much is *gained* in the understanding of the sexual activities of the normal adult, the child, the pervert, and the neurotic whose sexual behaviors all spring from the same source. The libido concept thus loosens sexuality from its close connection with the genitals and establishes it as a more comprehensive physical function, which strives for pleasure in general, and only secondarily enters into the service of *propagation*. It also adds to the sexual sphere those affectionate and friendly feelings to which we ordinarily apply the term love.

Before proceeding further, let us mention that in investigating the sexual development, Freud put down two guideposts for the judgment of sexual behavior. The first he called the *sexual object*, which he defines as the person from whom sexual attraction emanates; the second is the *sexual aim*, or the aim toward which the instinct strives. Thus, the goal of normal life is to attain the proper love object, and the normal aim is reproduction. If we now consider the sexual activities of the child, the pervert, and the neurotic, we find that they all originate from the same sources, although they differ in their behavior toward the aim and the object. The child's sexual aim is not centralized, for it can obtain gratification from different parts of the body, through so-called erogenous zones. The child gets pleasure through *aggression, looking, exhibitionism, touching, tasting,* and so on, as does the pervert. But with advancing age, these partial impulses pass through a definite evolution during which part of each impulse is repressed, another part is subordinated to the primacy of the genitals to be used for reproduction, and the rest is sublimated or deflected from sexuality to higher nonsexual aims.

The goal of normal life thus consists, first, in attaining normal genitality and, second, in finding a normal love object. If this evolution is interfered with, some injury may result to one of the partial impulses which leaves a weakness or a *fixation,* to which the libido may later regress and, depending on the particular component or partial impulse affected, it may produce a *sadist,* a *masochist,* a *voyeur,* a *toucheur,* an *exhibitionist,* a *renifleur,* a *necrophiliac* [9] or a homosexual. Such a pervert usually deviates from the aim. A certain amount of looking, touching, and so on is normal, and ordinarily forms the forepleasure to sexual union. On the other hand, the pervert does not crave sexual intercourse but is satisfied with the forepleasure. Instead of being attracted by a woman forcibly enough to court her, the pervert can get a full outlet from her through looking or touching.

The large homosexual class invariably deviates from the object and naturally also from the aim; instead of falling in love with a person of the opposite sex, homosexuals prefer sensuous gratification from one of their own sex by way of erogenous zones. In brief, all adults who deviate from the object or aim or both have been more or less stunted in their sexual evolution and, therefore, have brought along into adult life a fragment of their childhood sexuality; they have not attained adult genitality. Clinically, however, both adult and child are subject to the same neurotic disturbances if something happens to impede or inhibit their libido

[9] Brill: "Necrophilia," *J. Criminal Psychopathol.,* 1941.

attachments. Let us consider the case of a nervous child, keeping in mind Freud's dictum that no neurosis is possible in a wholly normal sexual life—a teaching that has aroused more opposition to psychoanalysis than any other utterance of Freud.[10]

An apparently normal girl of about four became very nervous, refused most of her food, had frequent crying spells and tantrums, with consequent loss of weight, malaise, and insomnia, so that her condition became quite alarming. After the ordinary medical measures had been found of no avail, I was consulted. The case was so simple that I could not understand why no one had thought of the cure before I came on the scene. The child had begun to show the symptoms enumerated above shortly after her mother was separated from her, and she was cured soon after her mother was returned to her. I cannot go into the many details of this interesting case,[11] but one can readily see that it differed materially from the case of the young woman reported earlier whose attacks simulated epilepsy. There we dealt with a disturbance of object libido or adult genitality; here we deal with an emotional disturbance based on a deprivation of mother love in a very sensitive or neurotic child. Nevertheless, it was a disturbance in the child's love life. For when the mother was forced to leave her home, the libido which this extremely sensitive child ordinarily transferred to the mother became detached and remained, as it were, floating in the air. She was unable to establish any new transference with the mother substitutes, and was cured as soon as her love object was restored. In the hysterical young woman the situation was the same as far as the disposition of her libido was concerned. Here, too, there was a floating libido, detached from the lost love object; but it was object libido in the adult sense, in which the genitals participated. In the child, genitality played no part because she was still depending on disseminated partial impulses and components in which the mother played the leading part. Nevertheless, we feel justified in saying that in both cases the neurosis was based on a disturbance in the libido distribution of the patient; in the

[10] The following case was reported in my introduction to *Freud's Basic Writings*, Modern Library edition.
[11] Brill: "Psychotic Children," *Am. J. Psychiat.*, January, 1926.

child it was infantile sexuality, while in the young woman genitality participated.

As to the relation of the perversion to the neuroses, Freud states that *the neurosis is the negative of the perversion.* I said before that the libido may later regress to some weak spot or fixation in one of the partial impulses if the libido is prevented from exercising its functions. If there are no obstacles to prevent this, if the ego does not exert any prohibition against it, such a regression becomes a perversion. In the neurotic, the ego strongly opposes any of the perverse activities mentioned above. But as the particular component or partial impulse becomes endowed with a superfluous sum of libido that strives to come to the surface, the neurotic, as it were, desexualizes it and instead of confining his outlet for example to looking or touching, he becomes afflicted with visual disturbances, for which the ophthalmologist can find no organic reason, or with some skin affections. In short, the child likes to indulge in activities that adults conceive as disgusting because the child has not yet developed the *reaction formations* against them, whereas the adult pervert has never developed them.

On the other hand, the neurotic who also brings along a fragment from his infantile sexuality, instead of obtaining pleasure from the libidinally accentuated partial impulse, like the pervert desexualizes his libido and then suffers from the negative or opposite of the perversion. The patient who struggled against the obsessive thought "God might get into me" (see p. 33) was first disturbed by the sensuous idea that he might have sexual congress with a dog. This was because he had been caught playing with the house dog by his ignorant father who beat him brutally and deprived him of the dog to which he was deeply attached. As a result of this trauma, which occurred at the age of four, he grew up as an abnormally sensitive young man who was particularly deterred by anything sexual. When the dog episode took place, the sight of the dogs *in coitu* was really stimulating to him. But as everything sexual was taboo to him, he immediately repressed and desexualized the feeling and made an obsession of it.

In the neurotic, as we said, the ego strongly opposes any perverse activities and as soon as the libido regresses to a former halting place and threatens to sexualize that particular impulse, it is immediately repressed. In the pervert, the ego exerts no pressure against such sexualization. The pervert's conflicts, if they exist at all, are based on social fear; they do not come from any endopsychic resistances.

Some perverts can, however, be cured by analysis, and some can only be helped to sublimate their perverted libido into something normal and useful. For *sublimation*, another term coined by Freud, is a process of deflecting libido or sexual motive activity from human objects to new objects of a nonsexual, socially valuable nature. Thus a *voyeur*, who had for years alternated between neurotic visual annoyances and scoptophilia which had brought him into conflict with the law on several occasions, after analysis became a dealer in optical instruments, a vocation he has been following pleasurably and profitably for more than a generation.

Sublimation thus also gives justification for broadening the concept of sex. For investigation shows that most of our so-called feelings of tenderness and affection, which form part of our actions and general relations in life, originally formed part of pure sexuality that were later inhibited and deflected to higher aims.

For example, I have known elderly benevolent persons who contributed much of their time and money to the protection and conservation of animals, who in their youth had been extremely aggressive and enthusiastic hunters of wild life. Their accentuated aggression was originally a part of their infantile sexuality; then, as a result of training, it was first inhibited and later entirely repressed and changed into sympathy for animals. Now and then we encounter cases in which repression and sublimation struggle with each other and present a paradoxical situation. Thus a man who was well known as a lover of animals was often seized with sudden attacks of rage while riding his favorite pony. He would beat the animal mercilessly until he was exhausted and then feel extreme remorse and pity for the beast. He would dismount, pat the pony, appeasing him with lumps of sugar, and walk him home—a distance of three or four miles. We cannot here give an analysis of this interesting case; all we can say is that the horse represented a mother symbol, and that the attacks in which cruelty alternated with compassion expressed the ambivalence of love and hatred which the patient entertained for his mother.

This is a brief résumé of some of Freud's contributions to the knowledge of sex which I consider useful for our discussion. Since 1910, the world, i.e., the scientific world, has become more tolerant of Freud's views and some have even hailed them as great discoveries. Thus the late Professor Raymond Pearl of Johns Hopkins University, reviewing my third translation of the *Three Contributions*, said: "Freud has made an enormous and profound contribution to an understanding of the meaning of sex. Out of all the bitter controversies which have gone around him, Freud emerges as a very great man with many earmarks of genius." [12] Another well-known and distinguished scientist, Professor William Morton Wheeler of Harvard University, states that after reading some twenty volumes on psychoanalysis, the works of Freud, Jung, Brill, Jones, etc., he "cannot refrain from recording a few personal impressions of what I believe to be one of the most extraordinary and far-reaching contributions to thought."

If some of you think that modesty should keep me from reading the statements of these two outstanding scientists, I wish to say that although times and opinions about Freud and his works have changed, I have not yet forgotten the hardships I went through for many years because I was his translator and exponent. So please do not begrudge me the pleasure of telling the present audience that I was not an enthusiastic youngster who followed a false prophet, as I was called in the first decade of this century before another large audience in this very hall.

[12] *Quarter. Review of Biology*, December. 1930.

FIVE

THE ZURICH SCHOOL AND PSYCHOANALYSIS

COMPARED to analyses of today, the technique we used in Burghölzli was simple in outline and structure. It was based entirely on Freud's modification of the cathartic method and on his analysis of a case of chronic paranoia which he reported in 1896.[1] In this analysis Freud endeavored to show that a psychosis, too, can be explained by psychoanalysis; that paranoiac mechanisms resemble those of hysteria and compulsion neurosis; that they are all products of repression and, except for differences in explanation, the symptoms of paranoia are determined according to the scheme of the transformation mechanisms of the psychoneurosis. As all cases at our disposal in Burghölzli were psychotics, we were naturally unable to utilize in our analysis the finer structures that Freud formulated in his report of the Dora case.[2]

As I have already stated, it was in this analysis that he first demonstrated dream interpretation as the most valuable instrument in psychoanalytic therapy since it led directly to the earliest years of childhood. But in addition to this technical procedure he also stressed the following new mechanisms.

The first of these, which he called *resistances*, shows itself in numerous falsifications and gaps of memory which the patient produces both consciously and unconsciously by displacing events and incidents.

Second, a symptom is manifoldly determined, and thus has many meanings. The same symptom expresses at the same time many repressed wishes and fantasies, or it represents now this and now that wish.

Third, conversion symptoms are determined by "somatic re-

[1] *Neurologisches Centralblatt*, 1896.
[2] Although this analysis ended on December 31, 1899, it was not published until 1905.

sponses" in the patient. This is a marked characteristic of the psychosexual constitution of hysterics in contrast to that of compulsive neurotics. The potentialities of the morbid manifestations depend on this factor, and have to be distinguished from the motives of the disease which are of a secondary nature. For once he becomes aware of the usefulness of the symptoms, the patient finds many new opportunities for utilizing them as a motive for becoming sick again. In other words, if the somatic response is accentuated, new symptoms may be added to the old ones.

Fourth, Freud called attention to a new pathologic phenomenon which he called *transference*.[3] As the repressed strivings are brought back to consciousness, the patient transfers his former repressed wishes—love and hate—to the physician, which the analyst must know how to control else it will cause many difficulties. He emphasizes that it is the task of the analyst to explain this process to the patient, and he must trace it back to its original source in the same manner as symptoms. Transference takes place in every form of psychotherapy, but psychoanalysis alone takes due cognizance of it and makes the process known to the patient. As the greatest resistances to the treatment emanate from the transference, its correct resolution is most important. For only after it is solved will the patient fully understand his real position in life and then become freed from the dominance of the repressed ideas.

Briefly, it was from the Dora case that Freud gained a new conception of the nature of psychoanalysis which led to most important changes in the technique. Henceforth, the unraveling of the morbid manifestations no longer proceeded through the analyses of the symptoms, but the guidance throughout the analysis was left more or less to the patient. Whatever came to his mind was taken as the theme of the analysis for that particular session.

I have enumerated these finer mechanisms which have formed the most important part of the psychoanalytic armamentarium

[3] Freud earlier discussed resistances and transference from a purely conscious level, in the *Studies in Hysteria* (p. 229), but here he speaks of unconscious mechanisms.

since then in order to emphasize the difference between the regular analysis of the psychoneuroses and the analytic approach to the psychoses. For the finer structures which I have just enumerated are not, as a rule, applicable to the narcistic neuroses. In our analysis of accessible psychotics in Burghölzli we aimed mainly to discover the meaning of the symptoms. Thus in the summary of my first analysis of a dementia praecox, which I did at Burghölzli, I said that what interested us most were the psychogenetic mechanisms of the symptoms, that more might have been elicited if the patient had been more co-operative, but that enough had been unraveled to show at least some of the relations between cause and effect and the part played by the repressed complexes.[4] Yet even such an analysis was not so simple as one might think, for we subjected every symptom to the same analytic procedure as that followed in dream interpretation. We usually began with the association experiment and after every complex was exhaustively studied, we discussed the case with the other members of the staff, and if some interpretation still seemed obscure, we sometimes consulted the highest authority, Professor Freud himself.

Here is an example from my first analytic case that will show how we worked: The patient was an intelligent single man of thirty-nine, a bank official who had gone through two acute hallucinatory episodes with a five months' interval between them, each lasting a number of weeks. He then gradually improved, so that when I met him about a year later he was perfectly clear but showed a well-defined residuum of his psychotic experiences. His whole personality was delusionally changed and he had no insight into his condition. He remembered well all the details of his attacks and he was quite willing to discuss them. One of his experiences was that an electric magnetic power or ether forced him down to the floor in an attitude of prayer and he had to repeat with great force hundreds of times the Lord's Prayer and the sentence: "Am I Parsifal, the most guileless fool?" (*Parsifal reinster Thor*). When I analyzed the stereotyped repetition *"Bin ich Parsifal reinster Thor?"* (Am I Parsifal the most guileless fool?)

[4] Brill: "Psychological Factors in Dementia Praecox," *J. Abnormal Psychol.*, 1909.

I found that the day before his first crisis he looked at some letters from the girl he had loved sixteen years before. He did not marry her mainly because his father stood in the way. She then emigrated to the United States and corresponded with him for about a year when he lost all trace of her. He glanced at one of the letters and was struck by the sentence, "I am in Pittsburgh, Pennsylvania, with a family, Thaw." He stated that these words obsessed him, so that for hours he was forced to repeat "Pittsburgh, Pennsylvania, Thaw." (The patient spoke English quite well.) On repeating this sentence to me, he said, "Pa., Pittsburgh, Thaw," and explained that "Pa." stood for "Pennsylvania."

For many reasons, which one can read in the case history, I ventured to say that the memory image of the word Pennsylvania could have been represented in his hallucinatory state by the whole word or by its abbreviation "Pa.," and that in his delirium he fused "Pa., Pennsylvania," into "Pannsylvania" and then into PANNSYVLania, the first part of which then sounded like Parsifal. The resemblance between Thor and Thaw was quite obvious. And as the patient identified himself with Parsifal in so far as his behavior to this girl was concerned, I concluded that PANNSYVLania Pittsburgh THAW
PARSIFAL reinster THOR represented a condensation of his former love affair which played a precipitating part in his acute hallucinatory delirium; for such condensations and contaminations are quite common in slips, dreams, wit, and verbigerations.[5]

I was quite sure that my reconstruction was correct and most of my colleagues agreed with me. Jung, however, was somewhat skeptical, and, unbeknown to me, he showed my manuscript to Freud. In a letter dated December 11, 1908, Freud wrote "Ihre Arbeit hat mich sehr interessiert, ich hatte selbst mit Jung einen Meinungsaustausch über sie. Die *Deutung* 'Parsifal Reiner Thor' scheint mir richtig, ich legte sie den Herren von Mittwoch Abend vor, die sie auch accceptierten, die Bedeutung versuchte ich für mich zu geben, sie könnte etwa lauten: Ist sie mir noch treu? Das Hauptgewicht fiele hier auf das fehlende Element rein-pure. Es ist

[5] Cf. pp. 69, 643 of *Freud's Basic Writings*.

richtig, dass Sie die Bedeutung des Vaterkomplexes für den Fall
noch schärfer hätten hervorheben konnen, aber auch so muss Ihre
Darstellung 'quite a revelation' für Ihre Landsleute sein." (Your
work has interested me much. I have exchanged views about it
with Jung. The *interpretation* of "Parsifal Reiner Thor" seems
to me correct, I presented it to the gentlemen of Wednesday
Evening [6] and they accepted it. The interpretation which I myself
have attempted to give reads about as follows: "Is she still faithful
to me?" The greatest stress would here fall on the element "pure."
To be sure, you could have rendered more prominent the importance of the father complex in the case. But even so your
presentation must be quite a revelation to your countrymen.)
About a month later, I received a letter from Jung in which he
wrote (January 4, 1909): "Bezüglich, 'Pa. Parsifal, etc.' kann ich
Ihnen die Sie gewiss erfreuende Mittheilung machen, dass *Freud*
Ihre Deutung vollständig billigt, und ganz damit einverstanden
war. *Sie sind also gerechtfertigt.*" (As to "Pa. Parsifal, etc.," I can
give you the information, which will surely please you, that Freud
perfectly approves of your interpretation and fully agrees with it.
You are, therefore, justified.) Having received the approbation
of "Allah and his Prophet," as we were then in the habit of referring to Freud and Jung, as well as of the Vienna Psychoanalytic
Society, I was more than pleased, and published the report. I mention this here to show that although we did not at that time go
through a *lege artis* analysis, we were not heedless in our interpretations. That was, however, the main objective of our analyses.
We rarely went beyond showing that even the most bizarre
psychosis was based on facts and good logic.

In his analysis of the case of paranoia, Freud construed the symptoms as returns of repressed material which, like those of compulsion neurosis, showed traces of compromise formations. The
obsessions had to show distortions, as those in my God-dog case,
else they could get no access to consciousness. What was peculiar
to paranoia was the fact that the repressed reproaches returned as
loud thoughts or voices. This Freud explained as a double dis-

[6] Refers to members of the Vienna Psychoanalytic Circle who met
Wednesday evenings.

tortion through censorship, which either replaced the original thoughts by others or concealed them by vague expressions of modern thoughts that were analogous to the old ones. Delusions that also represented returns to consciousness by way of compromise had to exert much effort on the ego before they were unconditionally accepted. The ego was forced to adapt itself to them.

As elementary as these conclusions sound in comparison to Freud's later formulations, they nevertheless contained more than the nucleus of everything that he expressed later on the basis of more experience. In Burghölzli, where we looked at everything under the guise of the complex, the situation was represented as follows: The defense reactions of the ego produced a split-off or a dissociation of some painful ideas and thus excluded them from consciousness. These emotionally accentuated ideas, or complexes, later obtruded themselves into consciousness in distorted form, or symptoms, and hence appeared strange to the ego. The mechanisms resembled in a way posthypnotic commands, and the whole situation could be designated as a mental flight. But, unlike the French school and others who had observed dissociation phenomena, Freud was more specific and showed also the nature and mechanisms of their content.

Let us consider a specific case. A married woman imagined herself pregnant, complained of being called bad names and of being accused by voices of having committed incest with her father. Analysis showed that she was projecting into the outer world forbidden but distorted desires to have a child by another man, or by her father. For many years she was aware that her husband was sterile and impotent and brooded over the fact that she could never become a mother; being of a schizophrenic make-up, she then attempted to realize her wishes by a flight from reality. What one could readily discern in this acute outbreak was a conflict between her ethical self and her instinctive needs. A less sensitive person might have obtained a divorce and married another man, but she rejected this thought when her mother suggested it. However, since her maternal instinct still craved another man, it revived a childhood wish to marry her father, a thought that was violently pushed away from consciousness and so was repressed. But because the force of the wish tendency was too dynamic and could not be kept in the unconscious, the repression, as it were, failed and the conflicting wishes were projected to the surface in distorted form as symptoms. The patient then lived in a *dereistic* [7] or fantastic world, altogether separated from reality. The reasons for the repression, the mode of repression, and the mechanisms of the failure of repression are thus quite obvious. At the expense of giving up reality, her strong wish for a child was realized, but not without inner struggles. But as dereism does not really satisfy, the patient perceived the whole situation as annoying and painful.

As a further explanation for the patient's later behavior, we used to say at Burghölzli that the disagreeable affect observed in this struggle was seen only in acute cases as a product of the psychic censor or of the conflict. With the advance of the psychosis, the patient seemingly becomes more and more resigned; through the mechanisms of *condensation, generalization,* and *ellipses,* the symptoms or the wish tendencies become blurred and sometimes almost wiped out, to such an extent that the patient appears apathetic and dull. It is this state that the psychiatrist of old designated as "dementia," but which Bleuler described as a state of complete dereism. It surely was not a dementia in the sense of disintegration, for experience demonstrates that the so-called dementia cases usually showed not a bit of dementia. Such a dereistic state, which is a precipitate of the psychotic struggle, is, according to Freud, in itself a sort of adjustment or an unsuccessful effort at integration. Freud preferred to leave it undisturbed; he did not at first advise analysis in such cases. He reasoned that as the dementia praecox process was in itself a sort of adjustment, albeit morbid, if it were destroyed the patient would be left without any support whatever. But when I discussed this problem with him later, I was pleased to learn that he no longer entertained this view. On the contrary, he felt that in time we would develop a psychoanalytic therapy for the psychoses.

Meanwhile, those who were directly influenced by the Zurich school now and then published analyses of praecox cases in which they strove to demonstrate what we used to call the "Freudian

[7] Bleuler: *op. cit.,* p. 45.

mechanism." This term was used by Bleuler as the title of a paper in which he showed the ubiquity of Freud's mechanisms in the symptomology of the psychoses.[8] We were all very much impressed when Bleuler said in this paper: "It is impossible to know the meaning of delusions without considering the Freudian discoveries. The content of many delusions is often nothing but a poorly concealed wish-dream, which by the means offered by the particular disease (hallucinations of the various senses, delusions, paramnesias) seeks to represent a wish as fulfilled—I say seeks to represent, for even in a delirium and in a dream, a person does not always entirely forget that his wishes are confronted by obstacles. The latter become symbolized as 'persecutions,' just as similar experiences of healthy persons created Ormuz and Ahriman, God and the Devil." Bleuler showed in this paper that the same wish mechanisms are also discernible in organic and toxic psychoses. Calling attention to the similarity of the contrasting delusions of grandeur and persecution in paranoia and schizophrenia to the contending forces of good and evil in all religions was the beginning of a trend of thought that was later seen in many of the works that came from Burghölzli. Jung, as is known, had been devoting most of his writings to mythology and religion —an interest that might be related to the fact that his father was a well-known preacher.

At all events, since then the psychoses ceased to be mere objects of description, and the influence of Bleuler, Jung, Abraham, and others of the Burghölzli school has gradually permeated the most orthodox schools of descriptive psychiatry. In the words of Freud: "From that time on, it became impossible for the psychiatrists to ignore psychoanalysis. Bleuler's great work on schizophrenia,[9] in which the psychoanalytic points of view were placed on an equal footing with the systematic clinical one, completed this success." [10]

As to my own views on this subject I would say that inter-

[8] "Freudsche Mechanismen in der Symptomatologie von Psychosen," *Psychiat.-Neurol. Wchenschr.*, December, 1906.

[9] *Dementia Praecox oder Gruppe der Schizophrenien*, Wien, Deuticke, 1911.

[10] *Freud's Basic Writings*, p. 949, Modern Library, 1938.

pretative psychiatry in Europe was then established. It is quite obvious to me why this new interpretative psychiatry took root. Let us consider first the psychiatrist. I said above that after a few years of examining and describing patients, I became tired of it. In the light of my later observations, I went through a mild emotional crisis. It was not because I did not like the specialty, as I found out later and as everybody who has followed my career will agree. In 1917, I wrote a paper on the "Psychopathology of Selections of Vocations," [11] in which I asserted that no one ever suffers a nervous breakdown from overwork, that the restlessness and dissatisfaction among our working classes which often result in strikes are not altogether due to causes generally attributed to them. It is not so much a question of money as of emotions. In other words, one's vocation, whatever it is, is really a libidinal outlet in sublimated form. The adjusted person works for work's sake—his vocation represents a part of his "cosmic urge," and he is normally unwilling, nay unable, to stop it. As soon as I began to find an interest in my work, as soon as every patient became a fascinating human document, I could not detach myself from it. To show how and why I became so devoted to psychoanalysis, I will recall my first experience with it.

After I had been in Burghölzli about two months and had mastered the elements of psychoanalysis, I was, as it were, accidentally impelled to test Freud's theories on a slight lapse of memory. One Sunday afternoon when I was off duty, I read a case history in a psychiatric publication which recalled to me a similar case I had published. I started to make a marginal note to that effect when, to my amazement, I could not recall the name of my patient. This was a surprise to me for I had every reason to remember him. He had been under my personal care for months and, as I shall presently show, his case interested me. After making a strong effort to recall his name, it suddenly occurred to me to use free associations which, according to Freud, would lead to the forgotten name. I soon realized that the reasons for forgetting this name fitted in with Freud's theory; namely, that we forget a thing because it carries with it something painful and disagreeable.

[11] *Medical Record, February,* 1918.

This patient had presented an unusual malady which necessitated my reading considerably on the subject; I decided to publish his case history, which was to be my first paper on psychiatry.

The patient was arrested in New York City for attempting to set fire to St. Patrick's Cathedral, and since there was a question about his sanity, he was sent to the Psychiatric Department of Bellevue Hospital and from there to the Central Islip State Hospital. My senior diagnosed him as a dementia praecox. I disagreed with him because after studying the case for a while I thought that the patient was in a pre- or postepileptic twilight state. My senior jokingly remarked that I must have read something about this in some *Dutch* book. But my diagnosis was confirmed when the patient's condition cleared up within a few weeks. He then told us that he had had similar attacks before, some of which had lasted from six to eight months. During these twilight states, he had *fugues* or *poriomania;* he always ran away from home and wandered from place to place. He always showed *dipsomania,* drinking to excess for days at a time, and always tried to set fire to houses. On two occasions he put his *pyromania* into operation; once he set fire to a railroad station, and once to a church. During one of these fugues, he ran away from his home in Canada, somehow got to London, and enlisted in a cavalry regiment that was soon sent to South Africa. After serving with distinction for a few months and being promoted to the rank of sergeant, his mind cleared and he then asked for his discharge. In normal life, he was an editor of a journal, a quiet, more or less henpecked husband; but during the crepuscular attacks he showed the reverse of his former self—he was very aggressive and lawless.

I had gained my psychiatric spurs through this diagnosis, yet now I could not remember the patient's name. I then proceeded to find the name by free associations. I wrote whatever came to my mind as quickly as I could on a long pad, until my hands became cramped. I then read the associations but could not make head or tail of them. I did this for hours and was thoroughly discouraged by the failure of the Freudian method. I was kept from dropping the experiment only because the reason for the forgetting did fit in with Freud's theory. There was an unpleasant thought connected with the case: when I was ready to submit the paper for publication, Dr. Z., the superintendent, who had heard of this unusual case, asked me to write it up for him because he wished to read a paper at a forthcoming medical meeting. I was terribly shocked by the request, but there was nothing I could do. However, on the day before the meeting, he asked me to read the paper to him, and when he heard me quote French and German authorities, and learned that I read these statements in the original, he decided that I had better go to the meeting and read it myself. The paper was well received, but my name did not appear on the program. Most people thought I was merely sent there to read it for Dr. Z. All these feelings, certainly of a disagreeable nature, were, I was sure, responsible for my forgetting the name of the patient.

As I said, I followed the rules and recorded everything that came to my mind. I saw distinctly my patient's features. Page after page was filled with the circumstances connected with the case. Time flew faster than I thought possible. I became aware that I had spent five hours of strict application and had filled more than two dozen pad pages, but I was seemingly as far from getting the name as when I first started. Now and then my thoughts seemed to stop only to start anew. I was most desirous not only of recalling the name but of testing Freud's theory. Of the many hundreds of associations I noted, I will give the following which will suffice to explain the analysis: On seeing the patient in my mind's eye, the name *Appenzeller* came to me. This was the name of a patient in the hospital where I was at the time of the analysis, and the only resemblance between Appenzeller and my New York patient was that they were both epileptics. The former had motor epilepsy, while the latter suffered from psychic epilepsy; yet Appenzeller persistently emerged from the mass of associations. Numerous scenes connected with my New York patient, as well as many scenes of my experiences in the hospital, continually passed in a sort of panoramic review. Some were especially persistent and vivid, recurring with greater frequency than the others.

Thus one scene, an actual occurrence, was especially vivid. It was of a forest fire near the hospital which consumed much of the scrub oak that grew in profusion about there. I stood watching the fire with Dr. M. when our superintendent joined us. Many rabbits driven from the underbrush by the fire were shot by gunners. As we stood there, the superintendent turned to an attendant and asked him for his gun saying: "Let's see whether I can get this rabbit." He waited for the animal to come within range and then pulled the trigger. A crack was heard, but the rabbit scampered away. Dr. M. and I glanced at each other smilingly, for nothing is so pleasant to a subaltern as the maladroitness of his superior. But we quickly changed countenance when he turned to us and said apologetically: "My finger slipped on account of the rain."

This scene persistently recurred from time to time, but I attached no more weight to it than to the hundreds of others. Yet whenever my supply of associations seemed to be exhausted and I started over again, the name Appenzeller and this scene invariably reappeared. I gradually tired of the whole process and wished to stop it; but despite my willingness to do so, I could not banish the numerous scenes from my mind. I finally went to sleep and after about four hours, I was aroused by the same association, over which I started mulling anew. The same name and the same rabbit-shooting scene reappeared. I again heard the superintendent say: "Let's see whether I can get this rabbit," and just then the name of the patient suddenly flashed before my eyes. His name was *Lapin* which, translated into English, means rabbit.

It can be readily seen that had I been keen enough, I should have been saved hours of labor. For this rabbit scene occurred twenty-eight times more than any other association. Being inexperienced, I overlooked the very thing that Freud stressed, namely, disguised and symbolic expressions. The rabbit scene symbolized the whole episode of the Lapin case. Dr. Z., the superintendent, attempted to get the rabbit, but missed it. I wish to add that although I spoke French quite fluently, in my mind "Lapin" was always translated into rabbit because my actual thoughts were in English. In fact, I distinctly recalled that when this French-Canadian patient came to the hospital, I was struck by his name—"Rabbit." If we now bear in mind the French pronunciation of

Lapin, we can see why Appenzeller crowded itself into my mind when I looked for Lapin:

APPENzeller the epileptic
LAPIN   "   "

It would be impossible to describe the great pleasure and satisfaction I experienced on discovering this name at about 5:00 A.M. I could hardly wait for the staff meeting to report it to my colleagues. "Now," someone said, "you'll be a Freudian." And I have been one ever since.

I recalled this analysis of a memory lapse, which I have reported before, to show also how this sort of investigation differed from the mere description of cases which soon became monotonous and fatiguing. In Burghölzli, every patient was a new and interesting, usually fascinating, study. I could truly answer those who wondered how I could listen to patients for so many years—about twelve hours daily—without becoming tired by saying that I am just as interested now as I was in 1907. Analysis not only helps the patient but the physician as well. For one thing, it broadens his view of life by forcing his interest into the whole gamut of human thought and action. The patient naturally receives more attention through analysis than through any other form of therapy.

SIX

PARANOIA AND ITS RELATION
TO HOMOSEXUALITY

THE most remarkable feature of the whole Freudian system lies in the fact that no matter how strange and uncanny a neurotic or psychotic symptom may seem, once the key is found to the distortions and disguises everything sounds perfectly logical and understandable. This is particularly striking when we think of some psychotics whose general behavior seems absolutely foreign to anything in ordinary life. This thought came to my mind as I sat listening to Freud reading for the first time his views on paranoia. It was on September 21, 1911, at the Third International Psychoanalytic Congress at Weimar, Germany, that he first said that the peculiarity of paranoia must be sought in the mechanisms by which the symptoms are formed, or by those that produce the repression. "We would say," he stated, "that the paranoiac character lies in the fact that as a defense against a homosexual wish fantasy, the patient reacts precisely with a delusion of persecution of this kind." Not trusting his own scant experience with paranoia, Freud had discussed the problem for years with Jung, who called his attention to the Schreber case,[1] and with Ferenczi. They were all struck by the fact that no matter to what sex, race, occupation, or social status paranoiacs belonged, they all showed as the central point of their morbid conflict *a defense against a homosexual wish; they all went to pieces in their effort to control their unconsciously reinforced homosexuality*.[2]

The newness of his interpretation was at first very puzzling and astonishing, but as I applied these new thoughts to a case of paranoia that I recalled, I wondered why some of those explanations which became increasingly obvious in my case did not occur to

[1] Jung mentioned Schreber in his *Psychology of Dementia Praecox*, translated by A. A. Brill, Monograph Series, p. 141.
[2] *Jahrb. f. Psychoanalyt. u. Psychopathol. Forschungen*, III, 52.

me before. For the patient, R., whose case history I shall presently give, had been of great interest as well as annoyance to me. It so happened that years before he was my patient we had attended the same college. I felt sorry that I had to testify to his insanity, and I also recalled with annoyance that the jury, which listened for ten days to six psychiatrists and many lay witnesses all testifying to his insanity, brought in a verdict of "not insane" after only fifteen minutes of deliberation. Yet in spite of my thorough knowledge of the case, which was now clear to me, none of the mechanisms could have possibly been known to me or to anyone else before Freud's exposition of his new concepts. For no one hitherto looked at the neuroses and psychoses under the guise of Freud's libido theory. It would never have occurred to anybody that paranoia had anything to do with sex.

For according to Freud, the development of paranoia, like that of the neuroses, is based on a *fixation* of a partial impulse of the infantile sexuality which was precluded from further participation in the normal evolution of the sexual instinct. As the development of sexuality proceeds on the path of infantile *auto-erotism* to *object libido*, it passes in its course over the stage of *narcism*. It is during the narcistic stage that all the active auto-erotic impulses become collected into one stream or bundle which is then subordinated to the primacy of the genitals for the purpose of finding a love object. Experience shows that the developing boy takes first himself, his own body, as the love object, and the genitals may represent the main interest in this love object. Thus the first choice is an object with similar genitals, or a homosexual object, and from there it proceeds to a heterosexual object. It is assumed that those who remain homosexual cannot free themselves from the desire of requiring genitals similar to their own in the love object. This is also furthered by the fact that the little boy attributes the penis to both sexes. Moreover, where the heterosexual love object has been attained, the homosexual feelings are not necessarily abrogated. They are simply sublimated or diverted from the sexual aim and directed to other uses, such as the promotion of social feelings; they may assist in the formation of friendships, camaraderie, and public spiritedness. It is known, for example, that all overt homosexuals who fight against their erotic feelings are usually deeply interested in human relations. However, those who sustain a narcistic fixation are in danger lest a mounting tide of libido sexualize their social feelings and cause a retrogression of their sublimation. This may be caused by anything that produces a backward coursing of the libido, or a *regression*. It may originate from some collateral reinforcement, such as a disappointment in a woman, through a failure in social relations with men, or through a general increase in libido which is too strong to be discharged by the ordinary paths. Any or all of these factors may cause a breakdown at the weakest part of the structure. Analysis shows that paranoiacs defend themselves against such a sexualization of their social feelings.

In other words, both homosexuality and paranoia are based on narcistic fixations and subsequent regression of the libido to this weak spot. But whereas the homosexual reaches the goal of object choice, the paranoiac finds this difficult if not impossible to attain; instead his libido becomes desexualized and regresses to the ego.

Having reviewed some of the psychological elements that enter into the formation of paranoia which, as can be seen, is only a perverted homosexuality, I will now illustrate the process by the following case.

R., thirty-six years old, married, schoolteacher and lawyer by occupation, was admitted to my service at the Central Islip State Hospital on August 31, 1906. He came by transfer from Bloomingdale Hospital where he had been for some time. The commitment papers stated that as a child he was supposed to have had a severe fall on the head which left no apparent injury. In childhood, he was subject to violent fits of temper. At an early age, he was employed in a factory where he is said to have resented his vulgar surroundings and blamed his relatives for permitting him to work there. He entered college at sixteen and worked his way through. He stood well in his classes but was not popular with his fellow students. He often quarreled with them because he assumed an air of moral superiority toward his classmates in school and in college. S. was the only friend with whom he seemed to get along. He graduated in 1898 and then qualified as a schoolteacher. Here, too, he did not seem to get along well with his principal and the other teachers. He was disappointed at not being promoted to teach a higher grade and suspected that there was a conspiracy against him.

He imagined that the principal and the other teachers were trying to work up a "badger game" on him to the effect that he had had immoral relations with some of his girl pupils. He would, therefore, not permit his pupils to come near him in the classroom. In 1903 he married, after a hasty courtship, and soon thereafter showed a strong dislike to his friend, now his brother-in-law, S., and his sister. He accused them of immorality. He also accused his wife of illicit relations with his older brother and his brother-in-law, S. These erotic delusions, in conjunction with many other delusions of self-reference and persecution, gradually became very active. The patient threatened to shoot his imaginary persecutors, and it became necessary to commit him to Bloomingdale Hospital. There he remained a few months, when he was taken home on a trial visit; but as he soon began to react to his delusions, he had to be returned to the hospital. One of his peculiar delusions at that time was that Dr. Doran, the physician in charge, was his wife in disguise.

When he was brought to Central Islip State Hospital, he was quite calm and natural in his conversation. He spoke freely about his condition but denied his many delusions or tried to explain them away. While under my observation, he presented a typical state of paranoia. Mr. S., his brother-in-law, was the arch-conspirator against him. The patient accused him of immoral relations with his wife, his mother, and Mrs. S., i.e., the patient's sister. He often imagined that I was his wife in disguise, and on a number of occasions he also accused his older brother of visiting him disguised as his wife. The following notes taken from the patient's history nicely illustrate the point: On September 6, 1906, while speaking to me, he said: "Suppose I should tell you that my brother who visited me last Saturday and Doctor Brill were both Mrs. R. [wife] in disguise. . . . Doctor, may I ask you a frank question? Did you really have an interview with me last Sunday, or was it only another case of Doctor Jekyll and Mr. Hyde? You don't look today as you looked then. You had all the feminine traits of Mrs. R.; today you are severe and you look like yourself."

He also imagined that some women made signs to him and were in the hospital for the purpose of liberating him. Whenever he heard anybody talking, he immediately referred the remarks to himself; he interpreted every movement and expression as having some special significance about himself.

It is hardly necessary to enter into the further particulars of the symptomatology of this case. I will simply relate the following facts: While I was abroad, the family took him out of the Central Islip State Hospital, against the advice of the physicians, but he was returned to Bellevue Hospital because he was very delusional and dangerous. After having been there more than three months, and after a long trial before a jury where five psychiatrists, his former school principal, his wife and brothers all testified that he was a dangerous paranoiac, the jury declared him sane after only fifteen minutes' deliberation and he was congratulated by the Supreme Court justice and the jury on the able management of his case. He then escaped to Canada, from where every now and then he sent mysterious or threatening letters to people in New York City.

One of his delusions was that he was a great statesman and that the United States government had appointed him ambassador to Spain, but that the "gang" in New York City had someone without ability impersonate him, à la Frankenstein, causing the loss of his post. He sent many letters to our State Department and on one occasion made an unsuccessful attempt to see the president's daughter, Miss Helen Taft, who, he said, had communicated with him by some secret device. He was arrested and returned to New York, but again a judge allowed him to remain at large. He immediately returned to Canada and then annoyed the Canadian government with crazy letters, so that he was arrested, declared insane, and deported to the United States as an undesirable alien. He was again sent to the psychopathic ward in Bellevue where I had occasion to examine him. He expressed his former delusions, but they were more systematized and complicated. His mental deterioration was now evident and he was unable to hide his delusions. He thought the president's daughter came to visit him in the hospital and had many other erotic ideas; indeed, the psychosis was so apparent that he was soon adjudged insane and committed to the Manhattan State Hospital.

The characteristic development, the delusions of persecution, the erotomania (girl pupils, his brother-in-law having illicit relations with his wife, mother, etc., the president's daughter, and many women who came to set him free from Central Islip State Hospital), and the delusions of grandeur (statesman, ambassador) present a typical picture of a paranoid condition.

One can safely assume that there was a fixation at the stage of auto-erotism and narcism, and a subsequent failure of sublimation of his homosexual component. I recalled how shut-in and seclusive he was at college. During the noon recess, when the students would chat together in small groups, he could be seen standing alone near some wall or next to S., his only companion. The psychosis became manifest as soon as he began teaching school. The girl pupils obviously reinforced his sexual strivings, making it impossible to control his libido. His sublimation became retrogressive and all his social impulses were threatened with sexualization. He struggled against this and finally succeeded in desexualizing them. His whole past history showed that he had always been a highly moral person as far as could be ascertained; he had never had any amours or anything to do with the opposite sex or with his own sex except S. I learned that the patient exerted all his influence to bring about the marriage between his sister and S. But soon after the marriage his attitude to S. changed and he became increasingly critical and hostile to him. Within a few months after his sister married, the patient married her friend, but his wife left him shortly thereafter because he accused her of infidelity with S., with his older brother, and others. When the psychosis was fully developed, he made two attempts to kill S., whom he accused not only of being the arch-conspirator but also of immoral relations with all the female members of his family.

But before he assigned the role of arch-conspirator to S., he thought, as we mentioned previously, that the principal and the other teachers were trying "to work up a 'badger game' on him" to catch him with some of his girl pupils. This simply meant that he had previously entertained sexual feelings about them, or that they unconsciously represented a fixation from an early age. Judging by his behavior throughout the years, it can be safely assumed that there was a conflict between his conscious heterosexuality and his unconscious homosexuality. For a time his heterosexuality triumphed and he married after a short courtship; but the unconscious homosexuality gained the upper hand, and he then began to accuse his wife of infidelity with those men whom he himself unconsciously loved.

But why did this most beloved person, S., become his chief persecutor? How did this reversal of affect come about? These changes were brought about by the ever present ambivalence of feelings coupled with the unfulfillment of his need for love. The patient could not become an overt homosexual so he strove unconsciously to bring about a sexual union between himself and S. through his sister, on the pattern of the early family romance. When this did not satisfy him, he made another effort in the same direction by marrying a friend of his sister. When all these efforts could not stem the tide of his attachment to S., he resorted to a defense mechanism in the manner described by Freud in the Schreber case which runs as follows.

When we accept the homosexual wish fantasy to love the man as the nucleus of the conflict in paranoia in men, we at once find that it is contradicted by all the familiar principal forms of paranoia. Thus the sentence "I love him" (the man) is contradicted by the delusion of persecution which loudly proclaims "I do not love—I rather hate him." However, the mechanism of the symptom formation in paranoia demands that the inner perception be replaced by a perception from without. The formula "I hate him" therefore becomes transformed by *projection* into "he hates (persecutes) me, which justifies my hating him." The dynamic unconscious feeling as a result of the outer perception then resolves itself into the formula "I really do not love him—I hate him—because he persecutes me."

In other words, the patient's effort at heterosexual and homosexual object finding having failed, the libido, narcistically fixated, regressed to the pregenital and anal-sadistic organization and the destructive or ego impulses were then permitted to become dominant. Instead of loving, he resorted to paranoid projection as a defense against his homosexual wishes.

Another point of attack for the contradiction is the erotomania that maintains "I do not love him—I love them." (R. always maintained that many ladies came to help him and that the president's daughter was in love with him, etc.) But the same impulsion to projection changes the sentence into "I notice that they love me." We then have "I do not love him—I love her—because she loves me." Many cases of erotomania could give the impression of exaggerated or distorted heterosexual fixation if we were not aware of the fact that all these loves do not start with inner perceptions of loving, but are feelings of being loved coming from without. Thus a stagehand who was committed to Central Islip State Hospital because he imagined that the well-known actress Maude Adams was in love with him, and consequently annoyed her with his attentions, insisted that she loved him first, otherwise he would not have forced his attention on her. He was, however, unable to mention a single instance to justify his statement.

The third contradiction would be the delusions of jealousy which were also present in our patient.

In the delusions of jealousy of alcoholics, we fully understand the part played by alcohol. It removes inhibitions and causes a regression of sublimation. *In vino veritas.* A man is often driven to drink through disappointment in a woman, and usually seeks solace in drinking places or clubs where the company of men offers him the emotional gratification he now misses. But in the predisposed individual, as soon as the men become objects of a stronger libidinal occupation in his unconscious, he defends himself through a third form of contradiction, "I do not love the men—she loves them," and he then suspects his wife with all the men he attempted to love. Our patient was a total abstainer and alcohol naturally played no part in his paranoia. But the following case will illustrate the type of paranoia in which jealousy played the most prominent part.

It concerned M., a married man of thirty-five who was brought to me because he was extremely jealous of his wife. As is usual in such cases, he was sure that his wife was carrying on affairs with many men. After I became absolutely convinced that he had no basis for his jealous feelings, I told him that he was suffering from pathologic jealousy, and he had enough insight to consent to come for treatment. But as it was impossible for him to refrain from nagging his wife with hundreds of questions concerning her whereabouts every minute of the day, I separated him from her. When this, too, did not help, and he made an attempt to kill his father-in-law, I sent him to Vienna. Professor Freud treated him for a year and a half, but when he returned to New York I found him improved but not cured. He was still under the compulsion to question his wife, although he had enough insight to realize that his jealousy had an unconscious basis. I communicated with Freud who advised that the patient return to him. He stayed another year in Vienna and when he came to New York, he himself felt that he was not yet well. Professor Freud then advised that I continue the analysis. I saw the patient regularly for about six more months, and I then suggested that he try to get along without my help. I am glad to state that he has now been well for about twenty years. Let us now hear what Freud thought of paranoid jealousy for which this patient's case formed the material.[3]

Jealousy, according to Freud, is a normal affective state, like grief. Everybody has occasion to be jealous, and if one does not encounter it in consciousness, "the inference is justified that it has undergone severe repression and consequently plays all the greater part in his unconscious." There are three levels or stages of jealousy: (1) *competitive or normal jealousy*, (2) *projected jealousy*, and (3) *delusional jealousy*. Normal jealousy is made up of grief, the pain at the thought of losing the love object, and of the narcistic wound, one's *amour propre* is hurt at the idea of losing the woman. There is also a feeling of hostility against the successful rival and a certain amount of self-criticism for losing the object. Although it is called normal jealousy, it is not always entirely rational, i.e., it is not based altogether on actual situations, nor is it proportionate to the real facts or under full control of the ego. It

[3] Freud: "Über einige neurotische Mechanismen bei Eifersucht, Paranoia und Homosexualität," *Internat. Ztschr. f. Psychoanal. u. Imago*, 1922.

is also to be noted that in many persons it is experienced bisexually. Thus the jealous man may not only experience pain in regard to the loved woman and hatred toward his male rival, but he may also feel grief in regard to the unconsciously loved man and hatred toward the woman as his rival. One of my patients, also seen by Professor Freud in consultation, suffered from jealousy fantasies wherein he identified himself with both his successful rival and with his mistress. He went through a regular sort of routine in his fantasies. He visualized the minutest details of coitus between his mistress and her paramour; during the preliminaries he hurled a thousand maledictions at his rival, while during the actual act, he experienced severe pain at every fancied motion of his rival, and then cursed his mistress for being an insatiable vampire. Such an identification is based on the more complete Oedipus complex.[4]

Projection jealousy originates in both men and women, either through their own actual unfaithfulness or through impulses to unfaithfulness that were repressed. In discussing this form, Freud indulges in a bit of philosophizing about matrimonial fidelity, the truth of which the average man recognizes but dares not express frankly. He states that the degree of fidelity required in marriage can be maintained only in the face of continual temptations. Anyone who denies this in himself will, nevertheless, feel the impulsion to it so strongly that he will be glad to make use of an unconscious mechanism as an alleviation. This relief, or absolution by one's conscience, is attained by projecting one's own impulses to disloyalty to the wife, to whom one owes loyalty. Social conventions have wisely taken account of this universally existing state of affairs by granting some freedom to the married woman's desire to attract and to the married man's desire to make conquests. Society expects that the indisputable tendency to infidelity will thus be drained and rendered harmless.[5] Conventional experience teaches that such little ventures in the direction of infidelity are not held against either party, provided they come home to roost, and in most cases it actually happens that the inflamed passion, fanned by a strange love object, finds gratification in a sort of turning back

---

[4] Freud: *Das Ich und das Es*, p. 42, Internat. Psychoanalyt. Verlag, 1923.
[5] *Gesammelte Schriften*, V, 389.

to fidelity at home. But those who are morbidly jealous do not recognize this conventional tolerance; they do not believe that one can halt or turn back once one has started on this path, nor do they believe that social flirtation can serve as a safety valve for real infidelity. Projection jealousy, to be sure, has an almost delusional character, but it is amenable to analysis in that the patient can be made to recognize the unconscious motives to his fantasies.

The third form, *delusional jealousy*, is more severe. It, too, originates on the basis of repressed impulses to infidelity but the objects of its fantasies belong to the same sex. Delusional jealousy is "an acidulated homosexuality and justly belongs among the classical forms of paranoia." It is an attempt at defense against a very strong homosexual striving and in man it may be expressed in the formula, "Indeed, I do not love him, she loves him."

Let me illustrate this by the following cases: A clergyman of sixty, married thirty-five years and the father of five children, consulted me about his fifty-six-year-old wife. He was sure that she was a nymphomaniac. But as he described her behavior, I became convinced that he himself suffered from paranoid delusions of jealousy. When I inquired if he had any proof of his wife's infidelities, he pulled a folded paper from his breast pocket and showed me a written confession of adultery signed by his wife and a brother clergyman. A psychiatrist who is sure of his diagnosis need not, however, be swayed even by such seemingly indisputable evidence. I asked him who wrote this confession because I noticed that the writing looked different from the signatures, and he said that he wrote it and they signed it. When I met the wife she told me that the visitor and her husband had been classmates in the theological seminary, that she had never met this man before the evening in question. He happened to pass through the small city in which they lived and her husband invited him to stay overnight in their home. He slept in a room on a lower floor near her two sons, and at two o'clock in the morning her husband, who had been accusing her of infidelity with many men for years, aroused her and insisted that his friend had just sneaked out of her bed which was only about six feet across from the husband's bed. He became very excited and forced his friend to come up and there he accused them of adultery. She said that she herself, having gone through many similar experiences, was composed and tried to calm him, but the poor guest was terrified when her husband threatened to prefer charges against him with the bishop. Her husband was willing, however, to swear by everything holy that if they signed the confession he put before them, he would keep his peace. She finally managed to convey to the guest that her husband was not in his right mind, and to calm him they signed the confession.

I later found that while they roomed together as students in the seminary, there was some homosexual playing between the two friends. It was undoubtedly a case of *faute de mieux* on the part of the two divinity students, for both married later and showed no overt homosexuality.

Here the mechanism was as described above; it followed the formula, "I don't love them but she does." With the beginning of her menopause, the wife had lost all desire for sex and discouraged her husband's advances. Somewhat later, he began to show signs of impotence and with it delusions of jealousy. The inability to gratify his heterosexual needs enhanced his dormant homosexuality which he repressed and projected to his wife. The fact that his former homosexual partner slept in his home undoubtedly recalled their past sexual behavior and provoked this attack of jealousy and the projecting of his own desires to his wife. The results of the treatment turned out to be quite satisfactory. Being an intelligent man, the patient gained sufficient insight into his condition and has behaved well for more than fifteen years.

Let us now return to the M. case which Professor Freud summarized as follows: "When I saw him, he was still subject to clearly defined attacks which lasted for several days and curiously enough regularly appeared on the day following an act of intercourse, which was incidentally satisfying to both of them." The inference is justified that after every satisfaction of the heterosexual libido, the homosexual component, likewise stimulated by the act, forced for itself an outlet in the attack of jealousy. The jealousy of the attack was based on his observation of the smallest possible acts, in which the unconscious coquetry of the wife, unnoticed by any other person, had betrayed itself to him. He paid very marked attention to all her acts: she smiled pleasantly or looked attentively at her dinner partner, she lingered too long when the postman delivered the mail, she made frequent visits to the school principal. "His abnormality really reduced itself to this, that he watched his wife's unconscious mind much more closely, and then regarded it as far more important than anyone else would have thought of doing." Freud then compares this to the behavior of those suffering from persecutory paranoia, who likewise cannot regard anything in others as indifferent, and they, too, absorb the smallest possible indications unintentionally offered to them by strangers into their delusions of reference. The meaning of the delusion of reference is quite clear: the patient expects something like love from every stranger, but he gets nothing of the kind. He is either ignored or he thinks that unfriendly remarks are passed; the preacher's sermon expresses an accusation or an innuendo of some sort. Freud adds: "And when we consider the fundamental kinship of the words, 'stranger' and 'enemy,' the paranoiac is not so wrong in regarding this indifference as hate, in comparison with his claim for love." The jealous and persecuted paranoiacs, there-fore, project to others what they do not wish to recognize in themselves, but they do not just project, as it were, into the air, where there is nothing of the kind already. They are guided by their knowledge of the unconscious and displace to the uncon-scious minds of others the attention they have withdrawn from their own. Our jealous husband recognized his wife's unfaithful-ness instead of his own, and by magnifying it he could keep his own infidelity unconscious.

We may also infer that the hostile persecution which R. per-ceived in his brother-in-law, S., reflected his own hostile im-pulses against S. Here the most loved of his own sex turned into the persecutor by means of the ever present ambivalence of the feelings which was reinforced by the unfulfillment of his need for love. Ambivalence thus served the same purpose for R., the per-secuted paranoiac, as jealousy served for M., our jealous husband, namely, as a defense against homosexuality. M.'s homosexuality showed itself in his whole behavior. He never made any friends or had any interests to speak of. Professor Freud thought that his jealousy delusions constituted his first actual relations with men. He had a weak father and an active mother, a situation one finds quite frequently in homosexuals.⁶ At an early age, he sustained a homosexual trauma. His shoes were stolen while he was swimming with other boys. The thief, a man of mature age, would return them only after the boy submitted to pederasty. This obnoxious and brutal trauma forced his homosexuality into repression and barred the way to its sublimation. He was his mother's favorite and married a rich girl in order to ameliorate his mother's lot. When he became engaged he had obsessive doubts about his fiancée's virginity (which according to Freud's statement was based on an unconscious longing for a virgin mother) but this soon quieted down and during the first years of marriage he was not disturbed by morbid jealousy. But soon after he stopped an illicit sexual affair, which had lasted for about two years, the jealousy delusion appeared and then dominated all his thoughts and actions.

When M. returned after his first sojourn in Vienna, I did not enter into any analysis of his case, but from a dream, which he voluntarily related, I learned that he identified me with his oldest brother who was a physician and who originally brought him to me. On his second return when he asked me to continue the analysis begun by Professor Freud, I soon discovered that he had always been jealous and afraid of his "doctor-brother." The latter was an aggressive individual who had displaced the father in the home. I believe it was this part of the analysis in which he made peace, so to speak, with his brother that gave the finishing touch to the treatment. I might also add that his brother was quite ill at the time of his analysis with me and died soon after I discharged the patient.

One may now think that the three links of a sentence "I love him" would admit only three forms of contradiction, viz., the delusions of persecution, the verb, and the erotomania; that is, the

⁶ The absence of the father through early death often produces a fixation on the father image, which favors inversion. In such cases the Oedipus conflict, which normally establishes the son's behavior toward his sex, is here lacking. In the case of weak fathers of the "henpecked husband" type, the same situation results because the son develops a deep longing for a strong, aggressive man.

object; but there is still a fourth form of contradiction which is a total rejection of the whole sentence. It reads: "I do not love at all, and hence I love nobody," and as the libido must be somewhere, the sentence is psychologically equivalent to the sentence, "I love only myself." This form of contradiction results in the delusion of grandeur which we conceive as a sexual overestimation of one's own ego, and which can be put side by side with the familiar overestimation of the love object. In our patient R. it manifested itself in his delusion of being an ambassador.

I have already explained the patient's delusions. I merely wish to repeat that in his defense against the increasing unconscious homosexuality toward S., he at first strove to become united with S. through his sister by the mechanism of *troilism*, which I shall discuss later, and by marrying his sister's friend. When these efforts failed, he projected everything to the outside and then accused S. of improper relations with his sister (that is, S.'s own wife), with his mother (his first love object), and with his wife.

I could not elicit what these improper relations were. Whenever I broached the subject, he became excited and uncommunicative. On a number of occasions, however, he directly accused S. of being a pervert and a degenerate, which points to the fact that he thought of some infantile polymorphous perverse activities.

Furthermore, just as he identified all his female love objects with his mother, he identified all his conspirators with his father. First it was the principal of the school (a father surrogate) and then some of the older teachers, his older brother T., and the physicians in charge of his case. As I was not a Freudian when R. was my patient, I naturally did not learn anything about his relations with his father, but I dare say that all the later persecutors represented the first persecutor. In this regard, the case history is incomplete, but the identifications as formed by the patient fit in with the general process of this mechanism. For through the mechanism of identification, patients can represent in their symptoms the experiences of a great number of persons; they can suffer, as it were, for a whole mass of people, and impersonate all the parts of a drama by means of their own individual resources. Identification is not the simple hysterical imitation but an unconscious mechanism. It is a sympathy based upon the same etiologic claims; it expresses an "as though" and refers to something common which has remained in the unconscious. We know that in hysteria, identification is often used to express sexual community. Hysterics identify themselves most easily with persons with whom they had real or imaginary sexual relations, or with those who had sexual relations with the same person.[7] The three persons suspected of sexual relations with S. had the same relation to the patient. We all know that mother, sister, and wife are often identified even in the normal.[8] He was once in love with all of them, but as they could not gratify him, he unconsciously turned to homosexuality, to S.; but as he repressed the unconscious homosexual wish feeling for S., he then consciously perceived not that he loved S. but that they loved him.

In other words, an inner perception was repressed and, as a substitute, its content came to consciousness as an outer perception after it had been subjected to disfigurement. This is the mechanism of projection. This identification also showed itself in his other delusions as the psychosis continued to progress. While in Bloomingdale Hospital, he imagined that Dr. D. was his wife in disguise and later he had the same delusion about me as shown by the following incident: I once made my night rounds after eleven o'clock, rather later than usual. He detained me for some time with many irrelevant questions. The next morning he wrote a letter to his wife, in which he said, "I am very sorry for having been so rude last night, but it was your own fault. Why did you appear disguised as Doctor Brill in a strange uniform, why can't you come to me in your own sweet form?" Why did he think that the doctors were his wife in disguise?

This question is very simple when we think of the mechanism of transference in reference to doctor and patient, with which I hope you are all familiar.[9] From my own experience with the patient, I know that the transference first took the same course as in any neurosis, but as the patient defended himself against this

---

[7] *The Interpretation of Dreams*, in *Freud's Basic Writings*, p. 227.
[8] *Ibid.*, p. 307.
[9] Cf. Ferenczi: "Introjection und Übertragung," *Jahrb. f. Psychoanalyt. u. Psychopathol. Forschungen*, 1910; also, Jones: "The Action of Suggestion in Psychotherapy," *J. Abnormal Psychol.*, December, 1910.

homosexual wish fantasy, he at first identified the doctor with his wife by the formula, "I do not love him, but her. It is not Dr. D. or Dr. B., it is my wife." But as the psychosis progressed, it was then transformed into the idea, "I do not love him—I rather hate him because he persecutes me," which actually turned out to be the case. After the patient was recommitted to Bellevue Hospital, he told me that I was one of the "gang." The distortion that took place in the projection mechanism was an emotional transformation; what should have been perceived as love subjectively was perceived as hatred objectively.

The mechanism of projection does not, however, play the same role in all forms of paranoia, and as it is also found in other psychic occurrences—such as in the normal—we cannot consider it the most essential and pathognomonic element of paranoia. Let us, therefore, temporarily leave the study of projection, and with it the mechanism of the paranoiac symptom formation, and turn our attention to the form of repression that is more intimately connected with the development of the libido than with the form of the symptom formation.

The process of repression can be divided into three phases. The first phase consists in fixation, which is the forerunner and the determinant of every repression. The process of fixation may be expressed, as was previously mentioned, by the fact that an impulse or part thereof does not experience what may be regarded as normal development and, consequently, remains at an infantile stage. Its libidinal emanations behave toward the later psychic formations as if they belonged to the system of the unconscious, or as if they were repressed. Such fixation of the impulses may already contain the disposition for the later disease, and above all the determinants for the failure of the third phase of the repression.

The second phase of the repression is the actual repression which we have hitherto had in mind. It emanates from the more highly developed conscious systems of the ego and may be designated as an "after-repression." It gives the impression of a real, active process in contrast to the fixation which is a passive backwardness. Repression affects the psychic descendants of those primary impulses that have remained backward, if by virtue of their enforcement they come into conflict with the ego or into conflict with such psychic feelings against which there is a strong antipathy for other reasons. This aversion, however, would not result in repression if there did not already exist some connection between the repugnant strivings to be repressed and those already repressed.

The third phase is the failure of the repression, the breaking through or the return of the repression. This breaking through results from the point of fixation and manifests a regression of the development of the libido up to this point. It stands to reason that there may be as many fixations as there are stages of development of the libido. More of this later.

It is impossible to demonstrate these minute mechanisms in our patient R. I was ignorant of psychoanalysis when he was with me; I am also unable to tell what happened to him since then. In his Schreber analysis, Freud states that even after the patient returned to society and found that he was mistaken in his idea that the world came to an end, he was nevertheless certain that the world had come to an end while he was sick, and what he now saw before him was really not the same world. Such transformations of the world are quite common in paranoia. I have known a number of paranoiacs who went through a stormy delusional period lasting for years, but who later seemed to live contentedly, as if in a different world. They evidently did not care for anything, as nothing was real to them; they had apparently detached their whole libido from the persons and things of their former environment, from the whole outer world. For the end of the world, as such patients express it, represents the outward projection of this internal catastrophe; their subjective world came to an end since they withdrew their love from it. By a secondary rationalization the patients then explain whatever obtrudes itself upon them as something intangible, and fit it into their new system.

Thus one of my paranoid patients, who considered himself a sort of Messiah, denied the reality of his own parents by saying that they were only shadows made by his enemy, the devil, with whom he was still in conflict. Another paranoiac represented himself as a second Christ and spent most of his time sewing on cloth crude scenes containing many buildings interspersed with pictures of himself and some of the doctors. He explained all this very minutely as his new world system, and although he labeled the doctors with their proper names, he nevertheless maintained that they were other persons. Because I was in the habit of taking notes on what he said, he called me "Secretary of State Brill," and the senior assistant was "Prime Minister West." The paranoiac thus builds up with his delusions a new world in which he can live. The delusional formations which we look upon as morbid productions are in reality curative efforts or reconstructions. The patients usually succeed in accomplishing this after the catastrophe, and in this way they regain their relations to the persons and things of this world. Hence the process of repression consists in a withdrawal of the libido from persons and things that were previously loved. This is brought about mutely and without our knowledge. What we perceive as the disturbance is really the curative process, which makes the repression retrogressive and reconducts the libido to the persons that it originally left. It is brought about in paranoia by way of projection. Freud, therefore, thinks that it is incorrect to say that the inner suppressed feelings are outwardly projected, but that it is better to say that what was inwardly suspended returns from without.

However, a withdrawal of libido is not an exclusive occurrence in paranoia, nor is its occurrence anywhere necessarily followed by disastrous consequences. Indeed, in normal life there is a constant detachment of libido from persons and objects without resultant paranoia or other neuroses; it merely causes a special psychic mood.

A former patient whom I have not seen for more than sixteen years, but concerning whom I had heard on a few occasions through his writings, came to see me recently. He did not come for my help this time; he just felt like asking me some questions. We spent a few hours together and I found him very interesting and stimulating. At the end of the period he wanted to know whether I had diagnosed him as insane when he consulted me sixteen years previously and whether I considered him sane now. I told him my diagnosis of sixteen years ago read "schizoid with some depression."

This forty-nine-year-old patient came to me first following the breaking up of a love affair of five years' duration. The lady, it seems, wanted to marry him despite their having lived together for years "as if." He could not get himself to comply with her request so she left him and a few months later married his best friend with whom she had been living ever since, so far as he knew, in a Latin-American country. When he first consulted me, he told me frankly that he did not want any treatment but simply wished to discuss his problem. I saw him eight times, i.e., eight hours, during which we discussed his problem only indirectly. That is, we talked and philosophized about men and women and their relation to each other and the world. The only time he spoke directly about himself and his affair was during the first hour; the rest of the time, as I said, it was indirectly. That is, he brought up all sorts of problems which in a general way had some application to his affair. He displayed no rancor or ill feeling when he discussed his situation during the first hour, nor did he at any time.

After I answered the first part of the question, I said that I would answer the second part of his question only after he submitted to a regular mental examination, which he was quite ready to do. He assured me that he did not want any written statement from me about his mental condition and, so far as he knew, that there was no question anywhere about his sanity or insanity; that it was purely an academic question on his part. We then spent about two hours together during which he answered all questions I put to him. I also gave him a neurologic examination and I then told him that I found that he was above average in intelligence and that nothing I found would classify him as insane.

My examination disclosed that for sixteen years, from the time I first saw him until his present visit, he had lived the life of a hermit, that he had not spoken to anyone except when absolutely necessary, as in shopping for victuals and in traveling. Following the breaking up of his love affair, he conceived a dislike for men and women, "purely on a philosophical basis," and decided to keep away from the world as much as was possible. Most of the time he spent in a small country place, but he also traveled for about six years, going from country to country. He spent most of his time thinking, reading, and writing. For the last, he always found a ready market.

In brief, the man was a schizoid personality who, on the surface, went through a quiet depression followed by an almost complete withdrawal of libido from the outer world. To be sure, he was in contact with life through his writings, but I had no reason to doubt him when he asserted that he had exchanged no thoughts with anyone through speech except when it was absolutely necessary. The withdrawal of libido as such cannot, therefore, be considered as pathogenic of paranoia; it requires a special character to distinguish the paranoiac withdrawal of libido from other kinds of the same process. This is readily found when we follow the further utilization of the detached libido. In normal libido detachment through the loss of a love object, we immediately seek a substitute for the suspended attachment, and until one is found the libido floats freely in the psyche and causes tensions that influence our moods. In hysteria the freed sum of libido may become transformed into bodily innervation or into anxiety, but in paranoia the withdrawn libido is used in a special way. We know that most paranoiacs show delusions of grandeur, and that the delusions of grandeur may themselves constitute a paranoia. From this we conclude that in paranoia the freed libido is thrown back on the ego and thus serves to magnify it. It thus again returns to the familiar stage of narcism in which one's own ego was the only sexual object. "It is this clinical fact," says Freud, "that teaches us that paranoiacs have brought along a fixation in narcism, and we, therefore, assert that the return from the sublimated homosexuality to narcism furnishes the sum of regression which is characteristic of paranoia." In R. this end result showed itself in his grandiose delusion of having been appointed ambassador to Spain by the president and that S., one of the "gang," robbed him of this great honor by sending an impersonator who looked and acted like him, but who deliberately disgraced him and caused him to lose his ambassadorship. Our hermit, mentioned above, never really withdrew all his libido from the world; he sublimated it.

SEVEN

POLYMORPHOUS PERVERSITIES IN PARANOID STATES

MENTION has been made of the Oedipus complex, with the mechanism of which you are all acquainted; I also spoke of the more complete Oedipus complex when I told you about the double identification of the patient who suffered so much in his fantasies of coitus between his mistress and the imagined lover. Now the simple Oedipus complex consists of an ambivalent attitude toward the father and an object relation of an affectionate kind toward the mother.[1] When the Oedipus complex passes away, the object cathexis [2] of the mother is given up and the father identification becomes more intense. These changes consolidate the masculine character of the boy and retain a certain amount of affectionate relation to the mother. Briefly, this represents the normal issue of the Oedipus situation. If something happens, however, that prevents the boy from fully identifying himself with the father and he instead identifies himself with the mother, his future psychosexual life cannot be normal, and frequently enough he becomes a homosexual.

But whether the outcome of the Oedipus situation, in both sexes, is to result in an identification with the father or with the mother depends on the relative force of the masculine and feminine sexual dispositions in the individual concerned. This is one of the ways in which bisexuality influences the fate of the simple Oedipus complex. But, as has already been intimated, there are other and perhaps more significant ways which can be explained only by assuming a more complete Oedipus complex. This form is twofold,

[1] *The Ego and the Id,* translated by Rivière, Internat. Psychol. Library, XII, 41.
[2] Freud used the word *Besetzung* (occupation) when he wished to express the amount or charge of energy with which an object or idea is invested. The English psychoanalysts translated the German into the Greek *Katexo* (I occupy).

positive and negative, and depends on the original bisexuality of the child. The sensitive, neurotic boy has not merely an ambivalent attitude toward his father and an affectionate object relation toward his mother, but he behaves at the same time like a girl; that is, he displays an affectionate feminine attitude toward his father and a corresponding hostile jealousy toward his mother. In the case of neurotics and psychotics, we are always sure to find the dynamic results of the more complete Oedipus complex. This can be readily unraveled in the neurotic, but in the psychotic, who also utilizes dereistic thinking, the situation is often very complicated.

To illustrate the homosexual processes in some cases of schizophrenic paranoia, I selected the case of G.,[3] a young man of twenty-nine, who first consulted me during the winter of 1925. He was also seen by Dr. George H. Kirby and Dr. M. S. Gregory and spent a few months in Crichton House under Dr. Lamb's care. For the last eleven years he has been a patient in a U. S. Veterans' Hospital for Mental Diseases. Mr. G. was the second of four children; he came between two brothers, while the fourth child was a girl. Without going into a detailed history, I will state that the patient was paranoid for years before we saw him. His main persecutory delusions revolved around his father who, according to the patient, had him watched by detectives. Wherever he turned, he saw his father's detectives. The patient gave the following reason for the persecution: His father had homosexual feelings for him (projection). His father never lived happily with his mother so he centered his affection on him. The patient frankly admitted that he himself had homosexual feelings and experiences; still, he was not sure whether he should accede to his father's homosexual wishes. His father never spoke directly of his homosexual desires, but he knew that his father wanted him to accompany him on a trip in order to find out whether he was willing to enter with him into homosexual relations. Realizing that I might not believe his detective stories, he showed me an affidavit signed by a woman friend, Mrs. D., before the American consul in Paris, stating that frequently while in his company in Paris she saw

[3] Originally reported in *Am. J. Psychiat.*, March, 1934.

detectives following him everywhere. Mrs. D. later corroborated this statement for me and added that the same thing also happened in New York. She insisted that she repeatedly saw detectives following G. and her. We were obviously confronted with a case of *folie à deux*. Mrs. D. was about ten years older than the patient; she belonged to the emancipated type of woman and was just getting a divorce from her husband with whom she had not lived for many years. She evidently was in love with the patient.

G. showed a tendency to systematize his delusions. His father was very active in the Episcopal church, but he was also mixed up with a secret phallic cult. In order to seduce him to homosexuality, his father kept on sending homosexuals, who made advances to him, and he invariably interfered and somehow broke up any normal relations with women that the patient attempted. G. readily admitted that he had had homosexual experiences with his father's "emissaries" and that he was "more or less" bisexual from early boyhood. As a result of being harassed by the father, he was forced to send him telegraphic messages, in which he threatened to take decisive measures against this persecution. Meanwhile, the patient corresponded, and I might say pleasantly, with his father to whom he was beholden for a very generous monthly allowance which, too, was elaborated in his delusions, since he usually spent it within a few days and then went into debt.

Concerning the patient's past history we can state that it was characterized by a marked emotional instability. As a child he was delicate and ailing and therefore received more than his share of love from a very neurotic mother; his physical development was normal. His mother stated that from early childhood he had always been willful and subject to tantrums of irritability and crying, that he did not get along well with other children. He was always considered bright and intelligent, but was a poor student. He did not like anything that required persistent effort; he showed considerable talent in drawing and as he grew older, he wished to be an artist. His whole development, manner, and attitude toward life represented the typical invert, which condition was undoubtedly favored by the fact that the mother was desirous of having a daughter when he came as the second boy. His mother also stated that as a boy G. was very sensitive and jealous of his father and older brother and, as he grew older, he became more and more secretive. He had a habit of hiding whatever was his and was suspicious of everybody. Sexually he was always very inquisitive and his mother recalled many episodes to substantiate this. She herself was a prudish woman and tried in every way to curb his sexual curiosity through all kinds of punishment. His father was a busy person, a successful man, and paid little attention to the patient until he was about ten years old, when a close relationship developed between them that lasted until he was fourteen. At this age, however, the father insisted that he go to a preparatory school far away from home, for which the patient never forgave him. He went through school with much difficulty. He hated his studies, wanted to be an artist, and showed talent in drawing and painting.

Following his graduation from school, he held a few jobs for short periods and then entered an art school in Chicago which he attended off and on for about two years. When the first World War came, he enlisted in a French aviation unit, later transferring to the United States Aviation Corps, where he remained until the Armistice was signed. His military service was uneventful. When he returned home, he showed a marked restlessness and soon decided to return to Paris. There, he led the Bohemian life of the Left Bank of the Seine; he was supported by his father and was supposed to study art. Actually, he idled away his time in cafés and restaurants. In 1931 he returned home and showed the paranoid symptom complex, which finally resulted in his commitment. At Crichton House he was well behaved but could not hide his delusions, and as his parents wanted him "to get another chance in the world," he was allowed to leave the sanitarium after about two months. He quickly married Mrs. D., who by this time was fully apprised of his insanity and of his abnormal sexual life. She, however, refused to be influenced by my admonition; she said she was not jealous, that she loved him and wished to help him.

All the psychiatrists who saw him diagnosed him as a paranoid praecox. Our patient's sexual life remained on an infantile level; to all outward appearances he was bisexual. He himself thought

he was about 30 per cent homosexual and 70 per cent heterosexual, but these "extremes," as he designated them, seldom gave
him any satisfaction, so that sexual indulgence was not a spontaneous activity with him. He was sought by inverts which ac-
counted for his more frequent homosexual indulgences; now and
then, an older aggressive woman or one of the slender, boyish
type caught his fancy, and then he had heterosexual relations.
Mrs. D. was of the latter type and showed some masculine
secondary sex characteristics.

From what I could discover about his psychosexual evolution,
the patient, like all schizophrenics, never detached himself from
his infantile polymorphous perversity. His ego was either constitutionally or evolutionally much below par, so that the Oedipus
situation never actually became resolved. On the surface he was
bisexual; that is, he could identify himself with both parents, but
on at least a few occasions he had himself flagellated, and now and
then he resorted also to other algolagnic activities with both men
and women. But in all these activities one could discern a definite
weakness; there was nothing spontaneous or clean-cut in his
sexual behavior.

Very soon after he married Mrs. D. he developed delusions in
which he involved her with his father. He (the father) tried "the
same old trick"; he wanted to alienate his wife from him. Analysis
showed that his wife was identified with his mother, his sister, his
sister-in-law, and with two women he formerly wished to marry.
All of them, G. maintained, had been under the domination of his
father. One of these girls "died mysteriously" as a result of his
father's machinations because "she knew too much." This antag-
onistic behavior of his father was easily traced to his early jealousy
of his father and older brother. The latter, too, was his childhood
rival. He fought him almost daily until the age of five. This identification continued because his brother was in his father's business;
he was his "right-hand man." Whenever G. had occasion to refer
to his brother he always added, "Oh, he does what he is told!"
In rational homosexuality, such an intense older-brother rivalry
frequently plays a leading part in the development of the inversion;
for it is well known that early childhood rivalry derived from the

mother complex may be later repressed as a result of training and the cognition that one can obtain more outlet through loving than hating. The erstwhile rival may then become the first homosexual love object. As mentioned above, G. first hated both his father and his brother, and later became reconciled to them. His close relation to his father was especially noticeable. The hated rival apparently became the first love object. But later when this had to be repressed and projected outward, the wish became changed into: "No, I do not love him—he loves me homosexually, but I do not wish to yield to him, hence he persecutes me." We have already said that this patient was fixated on his mother and identified with her; not only did he resemble her physically, but he had her temperament and, like her, he was artistically endowed. Analysis showed that the patient's protest against serving as a love object for his father concealed the infantile wish to take his mother's place with him or to share it with her.

Many episodes could be mentioned to show the co-operation of bisexuality (patient's effeminacy) and the more complete Oedipus complex in this double identification, but the denouement of his marital life will suffice as the best illustration. A few months after the marriage, his wife called on me and begged me to assist her to get away from G. She was fully convinced that he was insane and as a corroboration of it she related the following strange episode: About a month before, G. brought home a former buddy, whom he had met accidentally in a speak-easy. As a result of considerable alcoholic indulgence, she finally acceded to her husband's request that they all go to bed together. This situation *à trois* was repeated on a number of occasions for some weeks.

The patient then frankly told me all about it. In fact, he wrote out everything under the title of "Summary of Mixed and Diversified Sexual Experiences." The man, whom he called John, had had homosexual relations with him during the war; he was his commanding officer. Hence, he was a father substitute, and the wife was a typical mother substitute. Following the more complete Oedipus complex, to which we must here add the factor of bisexuality, G. lived through in these acts both identifications; he was the father and the mother. The patient's description of this strange sexual episode plainly shows the wish realization of the more complete Oedipus complex. He writes: "The best party I have ever had, without exception. But here is the most important element about the situation. I was more or less in control of things. It was my woman and I had the greater factor of masculinity on my part and I loved them both. She was not trying to get him as a permanent proposition, nor he her. She was clever in making me feel by her action as follows: 'You (myself) are the one I really am attached to; I love your friend as long as you love him, my universe is your universe and what you want shall happen.' "

Delicacy prevents me from quoting all the details as given by the patient, but anyone reading them can plainly see the unconscious mechanisms of the patient's delusions. He sought in every way to defend himself against his passive homosexual temptations, which corresponded to his early attitude to the father, by reacting to them with the delusions of persecution. At the age of six, he slept with his father on a few occasions and through the latter's innocent but rather loving behavior, the patient sustained a homosexual trauma which fell on fertile soil and undoubtedly revived his early infantile cravings for the father. Another fragment of the above description states that he also acted passively toward John during the "mixed and diversified sexual experience." Such a triple relation is not unknown in sex pathology. The French refer to it as *ménage à trois*, and the sexologists designate it as *troilism*. Magnus Hirschfeld states that troilism is a disguised homosexuality.[4] Nor is troilism altogether foreign to everyday life. Ten years ago, the most successful play in New York City, *Design for Living*, revolved altogether around this subject. The dramatis personae consisted of two men and a woman. The men loved each other and both loved the woman. She lived alternately with one and with the other. A third man, an acquaintance of all, came along and induced her to marry him. After she had lived with him for a short time, the two erstwhile lovers made their unexpected appearance, and she readily consented to leave her husband and go to live with them both. When

---

[4] *Die Homosexualität des Mannes und des Weibes*, p. 87, Berlin, Marcus, 1914.

her husband protested, she expressed herself in some such formula as this: "I love him (pointing to one of the friends) and I love him (pointing to the other) and he loves him (pointing from one to the other), and they love me." And she forthwith left with them. I do not know whether the author of the play knew our psychological concept of homosexuality, but all the essential factors of it were cleverly depicted. The narcism was expressed by making the two men look and dress almost exactly alike; they even kiss each other. The overvaluation of the penis, which is one of the essentials of homosexuality, the play expressed in the following witticism: the hero and heroine were discussing the criticism of the hero's play in the London *Times*. The heroine did not think that it mattered much, to which the hero said: "But, don't forget, it is in the London *Times*—it's the organ of the nation." (Explosive laughter from the audience.)

For obvious reasons no attempt has been made here to give the deeper mechanisms that enter into the analyses of such cases. Those who are interested can find an abundant amount of material on the subject in psychoanalytic literature. Here I merely wish to give Freud's contribution to paranoia and its close relative, homosexuality. It is quite plain, however, that the adjustment of modern men is essentially homosexual. Whether it concerns the struggle for bread or for women, men are forever rivals. The task of civilization, as represented through all religions, has always been to do away with rivalry and hatred. Christianity stands in the foreground in this respect. Judaism and other religions admonish us to love our neighbors as ourselves, and Christianity instructs us even to love our enemies. In the light of everyday occurrence, who dares say that civilization has been successful in accomplishing this task? Whenever some progress has been achieved, some pathologic homosexual tinged with paranoia steps in, forces a regression to the anal-sadistic level, which to some extent exists in all of us, and the destructive impulses gain control over everything. We must not forget that the whole Nazi movement was started by either overt homosexuals or by those who could not rise above the anal-sadistic level. Nevertheless, so long as the individual does not suffer from the stress of need, he can remain calm, but as soon as economic or sexual struggles reach a certain intensity, all precious rules are thrown aside.

Since the beginning of time, men have warred for hunger and sex. The ancient Greeks fought over Helen of Troy, and Genghis Khan's hordes overran the civilized world in search of bread. Historians tell us that the prettiest women failed to move these warriors. But the dawn of civilization began when the Sabine ladies hurled themselves between the Roman and Sabine armies and, by proffering love to both, stopped the armies from killing each other. The erotic or life instinct thus replaced the destructive or death instinct. For it is the former that unites and promotes love and, in sublimated form, all the great assets of culture. Pathologic homosexuality, while permitting much play to Eros, curtails its activities to a fatal extent. It is a narcistic outlet at best. Paranoia is a first cousin of homosexuality in that it, too, is an offshoot of narcism, but its regression to the anal-sadistic level enables the destructive impulses to push the erotic instinct to the background and thus makes way for the sadism of the death instinct.[5]

As I said above, I heard Freud expounding these theories on September 21, 1911, and I read my paper on the "Psychological Mechanisms of Paranoia," in which I applied Freud's concepts of paranoia to R., on October 24, 1911, just about a month later.[6] This was not difficult because, as I remembered my case, I could easily apply Freud's interpretation of Schreber to R. Dr. August Hoch, who was the new director of the New York Psychiatric Institute, opened the discussion. I do not recall all that Dr. Hoch said about these new concepts, but following Freud's publication of this work, it was lengthily reviewed by Eugen Bleuler.[7] After reading the review, I was struck by its resemblance to Dr. Hoch's remarks and called the author's attention to it. It was in this work that Freud suggested that paranoia be differentiated from dementia praecox (Kraepelin) or schizophrenia (Bleuler). He proposed the

[5] *Das Ich und das Es, op. cit.,* p. 49.
[6] Brill: "Psychological Mechanisms of Paranoia," *Medical Journal,* December, 1911.
[7] *Zentralbl. f. Psychoanal.,* II, 343.

name "paraphrenia" for both diseases although he showed that they differ in many respects. Thus in the light of the libido movement, both paranoia and dementia praecox show *repression, libido withdrawal,* and *regression* to the ego. But in the struggle between the repression and the effort at recovery, schizophrenia makes no use of paranoid projection but of hallucinatory (hysterical) mechanisms. Further, in the end results of these diseases, schizophrenia does not emerge from the struggle as victorious as paranoia. In the former, the regression does not course back to narcism as in paranoia which then manifests itself in grandiose ideas: the schizophrenic returns to the infantile auto-erotism. Hence, the predisposing fixation of schizophrenia must go still further back, that is, to auto-erotism. The homosexual conflicts are less seldom seen in schizophrenia. Bleuler objected to this and many other of Freud's views, but he concluded by saying: "One sees that this work of Freud leaves still much to think about, to question and to investigate. The best sign is that it is an important work."

Not all cases show the typical course of paranoia; some, like G., follow in more schizophrenic paths. The following case is interesting because I saw the patient when he was still in the acute stage of development, and I feel that the analytic therapy actually stopped the progress of its development, thus permitting the patient to make a good adjustment to life.

J. McC. was referred to me in 1920. He stated that for the past five months he had been very self-conscious, restless, and irritable. To illustrate his self-consciousness, he related that only a few days before he became terribly embarrassed when a cousin remarked, "Here comes the bridegroom," referring to his coming marriage. This remark rang in his ears for days; it disturbed his appetite and sleep and made him furious at his cousin. He explained that he was engaged to be married, but he was wondering whether he should marry the girl. To illustrate his irritability, he pointed to a number of discolorations on his face, the results of a recent fight in the subway with a man he thought had pushed him. He had struck the man, who retaliated in kind. The patient expressed surprise at his own bad temper. This was only one of many similar scraps within the past few months. On two occasions he had been arrested—once for attacking a man in the street because he imagined that the man made a nasty remark about him, calling him c. s.; the other arrest followed the subway fight just mentioned. On both occasions he apologized and was allowed to go, but later he could not stop thinking about the insults hurled at him. He even imagined that his superior in the office "picked" on him of late. He brooded over it for some time, but when he finally had an outburst over it and became excited, his boss assured him that he had nothing against him, that on the contrary he was very much pleased with his honest endeavors and steady application, and suggested that the patient was nervous because of his approaching marriage. This irritability and pugnacity toward his colleagues in the office became so marked that he was urged to take a few weeks' vacation and see a doctor, which he later consented to do.

Further examination showed that the patient was an only child; his father died when he was less than three years old, and he was brought up by his mother and a maiden aunt. He stated that so far as he could recall he was always very timid and never mixed much with the boys at school. He was a very good student, took all the prizes offered for scholarship, but was terribly embarrassed when he was asked to recite in class. He was elected valedictorian of his class but refused to accept it because he was struck with horror at the thought of speaking in public. He had only one friend, John, with whom he continued friendly relations after they left school. He was very fond of John; they both liked tennis and played regularly four times a week, both summer and winter.

About seven months before the onset of his illness, the patient went on his vacation with John, and on the second day of their holiday, while playing tennis, John dropped dead. The patient was terribly shocked, but soon regained his composure, had his friend's body embalmed and brought back to his family. A few weeks later he became engaged to be married to John's sister Mary. He had known her for many years but owing to his shyness he rarely took any notice of her. It was during the funeral days that a bond of sympathy developed between them. While returning from the cemetery he first spoke to her for any length of time, and soon felt that he was in love with her. His mother offering no objections, he proposed and was accepted. He had never had any love affairs or any kind of heterosexual experiences before this; he seemed to have no need for women. His only outlet was masturbation which was stopped soon after his betrothal to Mary.

In addition to his irritability and ideas of reference, the patient complained of a lack of appetite, attacks of diarrhea, constipation, and constant annoyance from belching and flatulence.

In sum, we have here a single man of thirty-five who never was an average mixer, who had always been very self-conscious, and who for the past five months had been particularly sensitive in his relations with men. The slightest contact with them provoked feelings of irritation and suspicion; he misinterpreted everything they said and did as derogatory to himself. To be sure, he had some insight into his condition: he was not sure that the man in the street called him what he did, but he was certain that he heard him say it; he was satisfied that his boss did not dislike him, but wondered why he forced him to take a vacation. Was this not a sign of his aversion to him? Emotionally, he was very moody, and somatically he showed a neurasthenic or rather hypochondriacal syndrome.

The patient was under my care for eight months and made a good recovery in the sense of social adjustment.

Psychoanalytically I found that as a result of a special constitution and environment, the patient was markedly narcistic and showed anal-sadistic and oral fixations. Instead of going through the normal psychosexual evolutions—father identification and the abandoning of the mother cathexis—the patient actually identified himself with his mother and showed a poor adjustment to father substitutes. His mother had always regarded him as an infant, watched over his diet, regularly asked him about the movements of his bowels, and occasionally gave him enemas. Consciously and unconsciously, the mother image dominated his life to the exclusion of all other women. He never did anything without first consulting her; she supervised everything, even his church attendance. An environment and behavior of this kind would suggest homosexuality, but with the exception of one experience at the age of six with an older boy, the patient never had any conscious homosexual thoughts or desires so far as I could discover. The primacy of the penis, however, was very marked, as shown by many dreams of women with male genitals.[8] For a short period during the last war, whenever he saw soldiers marching, he visualized their genitals, and at least once while courting his fiancée the idea came to his mind that she might have a penis. His friendship for John was undoubtedly based on a strong unconscious homosexual attachment in the nature of effusion of feelings, and when John died the patient's libido remained, as it were, floating, unattached, and seeking for another object. He then became increasingly restless; his sublimation for work and play was almost entirely destroyed with the sudden stoppage of his precarious homosexual outlet, and his infantile heterosexual outlet from his mother was inadequate for his needs. In desperation, he made a weak effort to get some libido from Mary, but analysis showed that this was really an effort to displace his libido from John to his sister who resembled him. In reality, he was thus still seeking a homosexual outlet. This accounts for the penis fancy in his fiancée, which obtruded itself as soon as he began to court her, and for the fact that with the beginning of this fancy, or very soon thereafter, his doubts about marrying, as well as his homosexual sensitiveness, became manifest.

The nature of his symptoms plainly showed that they represented efforts at regression to the auto-erotic and narcistic phases of his psychosexual life, when he was dominated by the oral and anal-sadistic ego organizations, or to the period in which object choice was not yet fully established. As a result of his anomalous environment—absence of paternal authority and constant feminine influence—the patient failed to pass through the ideal psychosexual changes, such as giving up the Oedipus situation through

[8] The patient never saw a nude woman, so that the infantile sexual theory of male genitals in all persons was not altogether obliterated. From artistic productions he learned that women have no male organs, but knew nothing more.

identification with the father; in brief, he remained on an infantile level. The symptoms of marked irritability and pugnacity, his somatic disturbances of belching, flatulence, and constipation, as well as the secondary schizophrenic phenomena—hallucinations and ideas of reference—showed the deep conflict in the patient's unconscious when his infantile adjustment was suddenly disturbed and he had to make an entirely new adjustment. Logic impelled him to seek a heterosexual object, but this he was unable to do on account of his pregenital fixations. The primacy of the genitals was not firmly established, but self-justification precluded a return to anal and mouth outlets. The patient, as was shown, never really reached the stage of genital organization, in which alone one can function normally. Moreover, with the mother fixation he could have advanced to genital sexuality and then found adjustment on a frankly homosexual basis; but owing to his pronounced schizoidism and the absence of a strong father image, he became schizophrenic. Instead of frankly craving men he showed, as it were, the negative of the perversion; he was annoyed by them, following the formula cited above. He attacked them because he imagined they did not love him, because they disparaged and hated him. *He reacted to the repressed homosexual wish fantasy with sadistic delusions of persecution.* In brief, through the homosexual libido which the patient obtained from John, he was able to maintain himself with other men; but when John died, and he endeavored to find a substitute, he was unable to do so and, as a result, all his social feelings strove to become sexualized and were then repressed. That he made a strong effort at homosexual adjustment is shown by his numerous attempts to gain the friendship of the men he assailed. In his own words, he was ready to "apologize and become friends." Thus, in the subway fight, when both combatants were put out of the train, the fight continued in the station until a policeman appeared and separated them, and the patient proffered his hand to his opponent by way of apology, but the latter struck him instead, and the fight started over again.

Analysis also showed that the oral and anal regressions manifested in the various somatic disturbances here mentioned were attempts to elicit mother love which was now of little help to him. Throughout his illness he was at times angry at his mother and blamed her for his entanglement with Mary. He evidently expected her to object when he first spoke about marrying, but instead she encouraged him. The aged mother, fearful of her own health, wished to safeguard her son's future. In discussing the matter with me, she was not at all convinced that Mary was the right girl for John, but as she remarked, "I want some nice woman to care for him when I'll be dead."

Here again we notice that the psychotic state was precipitated by a struggle between the patient's ego and the outer world. In consequence of a disharmony between his parental influences—religion, ethics—and his primitive needs, the patient was unable to adjust himself to the reality of the outer world, and his acute outbreak represented an effort to change reality in terms of his own wish tendencies.

I treated the patient for about eight months, three times weekly, and have since seen him on infrequent occasions, and I am glad to state that he has led an undisturbed and steady married existence ever since.

I have seen many cases of paranoia since 1911, and all those that were accessible to study showed the basic mechanisms originally expressed by Freud. But whether Freud's concepts have been fully verified by others does not really matter. The fact remains that he gave a new interest, a real code for the decipherment of this puzzling problem. Like so many others, I have since then looked upon every paranoia or paranoid condition as a mental disease in a person of a special predisposition who sustained a fixation in the narcistic stage of his childhood. This view not only brings paranoia into the category of a morbid entity, similar, for example, to typhoid, but it also throws light on the intricate problem of homosexuality which is of the utmost importance in the study of the development of childhood.

EIGHT

DETERMINATION OF THE SELECTION
OF NEUROSES

I AM tempted to discuss here some of Freud's works published between 1911 and his next major contribution to psychiatry, namely, *Mourning and Melancholia*, which appeared in 1917 and in which he opened a new field of research on the problem of suicide and the obscure forces of life and death. But as I am endeavoring to present here only his psychiatric contributions, I shall merely review that which is indispensable for their understanding. I will, therefore, give a brief outline of his very important paper on the predisposition to compulsion neurosis,[1] which he read at the Psychoanalytic Congress at Munich.

His main thesis in this paper is that, as in the normal personality, the neurosis, as well as the neurotic character, is due to a collaboration of constitution and fate, i.e., to what the individual himself brings along at birth and to the accidental experiences from his environments. This implies that the causes determining the selection of the neurosis are altogether of the former kind, that is, of the nature of the predisposition, and independent of the pathogenic experiences. To answer where the origin of this predisposition is to be found, we are reminded that all psychic functions, especially the sexual functions, but the various ego functions as well, must go through a long and complicated development before they attain the characteristic state of normal adolescence. Freud then speaks of the theory of *fixation*, and states that our predispositions to particular neuroses represent inhibitions in development analogous to the facts of general pathology of other diseases. As to the kind of factors responsible for such developmental disturbances, "psychoanalysis must here call a halt," states Freud; "it must leave this problem to biological research."

[1] "Die Disposition zur Zwangsneurose," *Internat. Ztschr. f. ärztl. Psychoanal.*, 1913.

Freud then states that investigation taught him that the order in which *hysteria, compulsion neurosis, paranoia,* and *schizophrenia* are usually ranked corresponds (if not quite exactly) to the succession of time in which these maladies manifest themselves in life. Thus, hysterical manifestations are observed during the first period of childhood, compulsive neurotic symptoms in the second period of childhood (from six to eight years), and schizophrenia and paranoia are first noticeable after puberty and during adult life. Although these two affections manifest themselves later than the others, they were the first neuroses that were accessible to investigation concerning the predispositions for the selection of particular neuroses. The grandiose delusions, the turning away from the outer world, and the difficulty of transference, which are characteristic of both schizophrenia and paranoia, have forced the conclusion that their predisposing fixation must be sought in a stage of libido development before the establishment of object libido, that is, in the phase of *auto-erotism* and *narcism.* Thus, these maladies which appear so late go back to very early inhibitions and fixations.

Judging by these findings, it would be expected that the predisposition to hysteria and compulsion neurosis, which symptoms appear earlier in life, would go back to a still earlier fixation. Freud then searched for such developmental inhibition, as well as for the difference between the phases of development, which would determine in one the predisposition to compulsion neurosis and in the other to that of hysteria. With the help of clinical material, he finally concluded that just as it was necessary to interpose a stage of narcism between the phase of auto-erotism and object finding in the cases of paranoia and schizophrenia—a stage in which object choice was already effected but the object still coincided with the ego—so in the transference neuroses it was necessary to posit another stage before the final form. In this stage, the various impulses had already been co-ordinated for object selection and the object already confronted the ego as something foreign, but the *primacy of the genital zone had not yet been established.* The partial impulses that dominate this *pregenital* stage of the sexual life are of the *anal-erotic* and *sadistic organizations.*

This new formulation was fully confirmed by the findings of others, notably by those of Abraham.

As was the case in some of the other of Freud's new formulations which I heard or read for the first time, I immediately thought of a case that confirmed this new concept. I recalled a compulsive neurotic patient F., referred to me for analysis by Frederick Peterson in 1911, who besides many obsessions and phobias had also been annoyed by chronic constipation. The patient did not at first mention it, and it was not until months later that it came up for discussion. He then related how he had accidentally discovered a cure for his chronic constipation. He once played with a spool of cotton upon one side of which there was the picture of a girl. He playfully rolled the spool and as the picture turned toward him, he thoughtlessly stuck a pin into it. To his surprise after repeating this for a while, he felt like moving his bowels. He then resorted to the following practice which he modified from time to time until he was entirely cured. He carried a number of large pins which he sharpened occasionally and every morning he locked himself in the bathroom and there he drew a picture of a girl which he pinned to the wall, and then thrust the pins into the region of her heart. As years went by, he varied the procedure. Thus, when he was in the country he would shoulder his rifle and go out into the garden, and by imagining that he was shooting Indians, his bowels were stimulated into activity. When he was too busy to draw a picture of a girl, he simply drew a target on a piece of paper and threw his pen at it, imagining that it hit the girl. Sometimes he simply indulged in fantasies of fighting which furnished the same result.

Once, while throwing his pins at the girl's picture, one of the pins went through the open window into the garden and, as children were in the habit of playing there, he became obsessed with the thought that one of them might find the pin and swallow it and die. It was the first occurrence of this type of phobia which persisted for years with many variations.[2] When he first consulted Dr. Peterson, he was given the same advice he had re-

[2] A. A. Brill: *Psychoanalysis*, p. 398, Philadelphia, W. B. Saunders Co., 1922.

ceived before from many other physicians, namely, to give up his law practice and go to live in the country. He was a failure as a lawyer, for when he won a case he was obsessed by the idea that he had influenced the jury unduly and then argued with his partners as to whether he should be compensated for his work. If he lost a case he invariably felt that it was due to his negligence in preparing the case, and that he should compensate his client for it. His partners were quite puzzled by him and finally brought him to a psychiatrist. Peterson referred him to me after he had lived the life of a farmer for more than a year without improving. His obsessive phobias were all to the effect that someone would be killed through his negligence. I say someone; he said hundreds of people might be killed in a train wreck because he discovered that one tree of a carload he had sold to a dealer was slightly rotten in the center. As he was under the impression that these trees were to be made into railroad ties, he was obsessed by the fear that this rotten tie might cause a wreck in which hundreds of people might be killed. He then gave the purchaser a bonus to return all the wood to him.

The same thing happened when he attempted to sell his other farm produce. One day he noticed a truckload of barrels filled with cucumbers ready to be taken to market. The barrels were covered with sackcloth tacked around with nails and it occurred to him that one of these tacks might work its way into the barrel and get into a cucumber which would then be made into a pickle and that someone would then eat this pickle and be killed by the nail. I knew well that there was no use arguing with the patient; but since he was a very intelligent man, I did argue that granted that this nail might remain in the cucumber throughout the numerous processes it takes to make a pickle out of it, the nail was three-quarters of an inch long and anyone who cut the pickle into pieces would be sure to detect the nail. His ready answer was, "Yes, an American might cut it into pieces, but a Dutchman might swallow the whole pickle." There was no argument; someone had to be killed.

In brief, here was a case that confirmed the predisposition to compulsion neurosis as due to a fixation in the anal-sadistic pregenital stage. This case was also an excellent illustration of what we noted above, namely, that the neurotic symptom was the negative of the perversion. The catastrophic situations that the patient expressed in his obsessive phobias represent an extreme form of repressed sadism.

It is also in the paper on compulsion neuroses that Freud attempted to correlate his views biologically. He called attention to the fact that the contrast of male and female, which becomes firmly established by the function of reproduction, does not as yet exist during the stage of pregenital object choice. Instead, there is the contrasting striving of active and passive aims which ultimately become resolved into the difference of the sexes. The activity is controlled by the mastery impulse (*Bemächtigungstrieb*) which forms part of important normal functions but which turns into sadism when it is exaggerated in the sexual functions. On the other hand, the passive element is fed by the erotism of the anal-erogenous zone which corresponds to the former undifferentiated cloaca.[3] If this anal-erotism becomes accentuated in man, it may produce a predisposition to homosexuality in the next stage of the sexual organization, when the primacy of the genitals becomes established. The erection of this last phase over the former phases with the concomitant libido transformation provides the most interesting problems for analytic research.

Freud emphasizes again the importance of a pregenital organization of the sexual life and the close relation between health, perversion, and neurosis. "Psychoanalysis stands and falls," he said, "with the recognition of the sexual partial impulses, the erogenous zones, and the broadening of the concept 'sexual function,' in contradistinction to the narrower one of 'genital function.'"[4] He adds that the observation gained from the normal development of the child in itself confirms this view.

It is also in this paper that Freud clarifies the sharp distinction between a compulsion neurosis and a compulsive neurotic char-

[3] It is presupposed that the reader has a good knowledge of Freud's views as given in his *Three Contributions to the Theory of Sex*, in his *Basic Writings*.

[4] *Studien zur Psychoanalyse der Neurosen*, p. 11, Internat. Psychoanalyt. Verlag, Wien, 1926.

acter, by calling attention to the fact that what is peculiar to the neurosis, namely, the failure of repression and emergence to consciousness of the repressed material, is lacking in character formation. In the latter, there is either no repression or the repressed material attains its goal smoothly by substitutive formations and sublimations. It is especially in the sphere of character development that one sees a good analogy to the neuroses. Thus after the menopause some women undergo a definite change of character contrary to their former good and generous nature; they become crabbed, nagging, domineering, petty, and miserly; that is, they evince typical sadistic and anal-erotic traits which were entirely absent before. Such change of character through a regression of the sexual life to a pregenital anal-sadistic level corresponds to what is found as the predisposition to compulsion neurosis. Such behavior is thus not only the precursor of the genital phase but often enough also its successor and resolvent after the genitals have fulfilled their function. Hence both compulsion neurosis and character transformation are influenced by regression. The latter represents a full regression following a calmly achieved repression or suppression while the neurosis is the result of a conflict that strives to hinder the regression through reaction formations as well as through symptom formations. The latter are the results of a compromise of contrary tendencies and a conscious and unconscious splitting of the psychic activities.

The following case shows how such a transformation of character sometimes occurs: Miss X was one of three so-called "poison-pen" cases I have seen throughout my long practice. Three young women, all first cousins, had been the victims of some unknown malefactor who tried, with considerable success, to alienate any man who showed an active interest in them. Although the young ladies were related, they were not very intimate and throughout a period of about two years, during which they were the victims of this persecution, none knew what happened to the other.

As soon as one of these young women was seen with a man a few times, the man received a number of letters warning him against further relations with her. As a rule, the man suddenly broke off all relations with the young lady, giving no reason for his actions. The reason why the young men were so readily influenced by these anonymous notes was because they always contained something about the girl which, on investigation, proved more or less true. Thus one of these missives stated that the young woman had been courted before by a few young men and that each of them dropped her because "she gets fits." The truth of the matter was that in her early youth the girl in question once fainted. Other letters insinuated that the girl's father had been a convicted criminal when, as a matter of fact, he had some tax difficulty which was finally decided by the court in his favor. Still another letter said that the girl made some derogatory remarks about this young man, or that she was interested only in his money. All these letters always showed a more or less intimate knowledge of the young woman's past, giving details about her family and school life. Finally, the father of one of the girls discovered that it was his older daughter who wrote these "poison-pen" notes about his younger daughter and her two cousins.

There is no need to give the details of the discovery. The writer was brought to me for examination. She was a woman of thirty-six, single, who at the time of the discovery did not live at home with her parents. Briefly her history was as follows: She was an attractive young woman when she graduated from college at twenty-two. She was in love with a very desirable man but for some reason her parents refused to let her marry him. She therefore carried on a clandestine affair with him for several years, when he went out of her life under rather tragic circumstances. Two years later, she went through an abortion which was followed by an infection which later necessitated the removal of her internal genitalia. This brought on not only a premature menopause but a definite change of character. Instead of her former attractive personality, she now was morose and crabbed. She neglected her person and showed no interest in life. Most of the time she stayed at home helping slightly with the housework. She became bitter against the world and especially against her mother, so that it finally became necessary to keep her away from home. She then lived with first one aunt and then another but could not get along with either of them. She tried to work but could not keep any position for more than a few weeks. Meanwhile, her sister, younger by twelve years, grew up to be an attractive and popular young woman. X was consumed with envy and jealousy at the sight of her sister and two cousins of the same age. One day after feeling herself neglected and outraged, following a scene with her mother with whom she quarreled because she had refused to let her marry the man she loved, it occurred to her to write these letters. She had nothing against her sister or her cousins except jealousy and a wish to harm her parents. Henceforth, she spent most of her leisure time in revenge fantasies which she put into operation by writing the "poison-pen" letters.

One may think that Miss X could have become misanthropic and revengeful even if she had not gone through an artificial menopause, but as I had studied her for many months, I became convinced that the latter played a great part in the change of her character. For what depressed her most was not the loss of her good looks but the feeling that she no longer had any right to try to attract any men as she could not bear any children. In brief, I felt that as a result of her premature menopause, there was a definite regression to the anal-sadistic level with the corresponding character traits.

Professor Freud admits that the theory of a pregenital sexual organization shows two shortcomings. First, it gives hardly any consideration to the behavior of other partial impulses; it merely stresses the striking primacy of sadism and anal-erotism. Thus he spoke of curiosity which often gives the impression of being able to replace sadism in the mechanism of compulsion neurosis. For curiosity is, fundamentally, only a sublimated offshoot of the mastery impulse raised to intellectuality; its rejection in the form of doubt assumes much space in the picture of compulsion neurosis.

The second deficiency, he thought, was even more important. We know that the genetic history of a predisposition to a neurosis is complete only if it takes as much consideration of the phase of ego development in which the fixation occurs as of the libido development, whereas the above-mentioned theory takes cognizance only of the latter. It does not contain the developmental stages of the ego impulses.[5]

Following a suggestion by Ferenczi, Freud ventured to say that the predisposition to compulsion neurosis may lie in a premature advance of the ego development ahead of the libido development. Such haste on the part of the ego impulses would force the formation of object selection before the sexual functions have as yet attained full maturity, and in this way leave a fixation in the pregenital sexual organization. Considering that compulsive neurotics must develop a super-morality in order to defend their love object against the hostility lurking behind it, Freud felt inclined to assume that a certain degree of premature ego development is typical of human nature, and that the capacity for the origin of morality is to be found in the fact that in point of development, hate is the precursor of love. Perhaps this is what Stekel meant when he said that hate and not love is the primary feeling between human beings.

As to the predisposition to hysteria, one can see from the above discussion that there is a close relation between this condition and the last phase of libido development, which is characterized by the primacy of the genitals and the beginning of the reproductive functions. In hysteria, the latter become repressed but without any regression to the pregenital stage of sexuality. It is not difficult, however, to demonstrate that a different regression to an earlier *niveau* occurs also in hysteria. For the sexuality of the female child is dominated by an organ that is essentially male, namely, the clitoris, which in early life behaves for the most part as the penis in the boy. A final shift in development at the time of puberty must abrogate this masculine sexuality and raise the vagina, a derivative of the cloaca, to the principal erogenous zone.[6] It is usually found that in the hysterical neuroses of women there occurs a reactivation of this repressed male sexuality and that the ego-syntonic impulses defend themselves against it.

If time and space permitted, one could cite any number of cases

---

[5] *Internat. Ztschr. f. Psychoanal.*, I, 531.
[6] *Three Contributions to the Theory of Sex*, in *Freud's Basic Writings.*

to illustrate all the points made by Freud in his important contribution to the genesis of the neuroses. No one can do analysis without a thorough mastery of the principles advanced in this paper. It throws real light on the deepest mechanisms of the neuroses and brings them into close relationship with the psychoses and with normal development.

NINE

THE STRUGGLE OF THE PSYCHIC FORCES IN THE NEUROSES

I HAVE now given, I believe, enough of Freud's psychology to venture into some of his metapsychological works. Please do not be awed by this term; it has nothing to do with the ordinary concept of metaphysics which, according to some, borders on mysticism. Between 1913 and 1917, Freud wrote a number of papers that dealt with the amplification and further elucidation of the psychoanalytic mechanisms. Let us quote Freud's own words: "I propose that when we succeed in describing a psychic process, in its *dynamic, topographic*, and *economic* relationship, we should designate it as a metapsychological presentation." There is nothing fundamentally new in these papers for those who are acquainted with all his other works. All these mechanisms are already described in the first chapter of the *Studies in Hysteria*. The affective or emotional elements are emphasized there when the symptom is considered as the result of a strangulation or a damming-up of the affects, i.e., the *dynamic factor*. The differentiation between conscious and unconscious processes stresses the *topographic factor*, and the statement that a symptom results from a conversion or a transformation of a sum of energy that belongs elsewhere emphasizes the *economic factor*. Indeed, when one reads any of Freud's analyses, one readily finds all these divisions; however, he delves much deeper into these factors in the metapsychological papers.

Freud's original intention was to write a book under the title, "Prolegomena to Metapsychology," or "Preliminary Material for the Clarification and Amplification of the Theoretical Studies of Psychoanalysis." As was his habit, he then wrote six separate papers, which were published in the *Internationale Zeitschrift für Psychoanalyse* during the years 1913-1917. For some reason they were never collected into a book, but they were all reprinted in his *Gesammelte Schriften*.[1] Nor can we restrict the term metapsychology to the six papers for which it was originally coined. All we can say is that these papers—"Some Remarks on the Unconscious in Psychoanalysis" (1913), "Instincts and Their Vicissitudes," "Repression," "The Unconscious" (1915), "Metapsychological Supplement to the Theory of Dreams," and "Mourning and Melancholia" (1916–1917)—formed the beginning of supplementary and profounder studies of former theories and views, as well as of his later works. As I said, it is the last of these, "Mourning and Melancholia," that I shall discuss, but in order to make it readily comprehensible, I have decided to present first a brief outline of Professor Freud's formulation of the psychic personality, which in a way epitomizes all the works mentioned above.

Toward the end of the last and in the early part of the present century much was said and written about mental dissociation, splitting of personality, and multiple personality. In this country, Drs. Morton Prince, Boris Sidis, and others supplemented the French works of Pierre Janet on this subject and left us a rather imposing literature. The cases they reported showed that the ego is capable of splitting temporarily or permanently. Professor Bleuler discarded the term "dementia praecox" and substituted for it "schizophrenia," because he maintained justly that the main characteristic of this malady is neither a dementia nor a precocity but a splitting of the personality—a dissociation or a schizoidism.[2] In the gradual development of his theories of the instincts, Freud, too, paid much attention to the normal and abnormal manifestations of the ego,[3] and in his book, *The Ego and the Id*, he gives for the first time a theoretical scheme of the mental apparatus and describes the various forces operating in normal and abnormal behavior. He tells us that the mental personality is made up of three strata: an *id*, an *ego*, and a *superego*. The child brings with it at birth an unorganized, in our sense a lawless, mentality which Freud calls the id. Later a part of this id, which comes in con-

---

[1] In English, *Collected Papers*, translated by Rivière, London, Hogarth Press, vol. IV.

[2] Bleuler: *op. cit.*

[3] Cf. Freud: *Beyond the Pleasure Principle*, and *The Ego and the Id*, London, Internat. Psychoanalytic Publications.

tact with the outer world through the sensory system and thus learns something about the danger and hostility of the environment, becomes modified into the ego, and still later a part of the ego itself undergoes a change and is then designated as the superego or the ideal ego. The last evolution is especially characteristic of man.

Throughout all his writings, Freud, like all psychiatrists, always begins with the pathologic and gradually traces it back to the so-called normal; he follows the same scheme in the formulation of the mental apparatus. He starts with the so-called delusions of observation, which are quite common in paranoid schizophrenics. Such patients believe they are being watched, that they hear their own thoughts saying, "Now he walks, now he wants to drink, now he is going to undress," and so on. Hearing one's thoughts in this fashion is not yet tantamount to delusions of persecution, but it suggests that the patient is mistrusted, that someone is watching him, and that he will be punished. As a rule, these ideas sooner or later change into delusions of persecution. This power of self-observation, which seems to be separated from the rest of the ego, exists also in the normal structure of the ego. We all have the faculty of observing ourselves and often do so, usually in criticizing ourselves. It is, however, safe to assume that one of the functions of this force is that which we call "conscience." "There is hardly anything else in us," says Freud, "which we so regularly separate from our ego, and with which we so readily contrast, as our conscience." [4]

Thus, if one feels inclined to do something because it promises a great deal of pleasure but refrains from doing it, it is because conscience does not permit it, or if one should put it into operation, he may then be tortured by the pangs of conscience. Professor Freud designates this force of the ego as the superego, or ideal ego. This assumption can be readily confirmed through psychopathology, especially in cases of melancholia where one observes a definite struggle between the ego and the superego, or conscience. Ordinarily, when we have cause to criticize ourselves,

[4] *Neue Folge der Vorlesungen*, p. 84.

we usually mitigate it by some sort of excuse—we try to justify our conduct; but in melancholia, the ego humbly submits to the criticisms and tyrannical oppression of the superego and admits its guilt. An example of this type of psychosis is found in the case of a married woman of fifty-three who showed the following symptoms: She had been agitated and depressed for about four months, and made three suicidal attempts. She thought that she had killed her mother because she had not given her enough attention during her last illness, that she had ruined her husband and children because she had not confessed before marriage that she had once played sexually with her first fiancé. She wished to kill herself because she was unworthy of forgiveness and deserved to die. Here one could readily see that the delusions were the expression of a need for punishment. The whole picture represented a state of tension between the ego and the superego, in which the ego readily admitted its guilt and expected punishment.

I have known this patient for fifteen years and have seen her in four different depressions. I diagnosed her case as one of manic-depressive psychosis, although the last attack resembled involution melancholia. Investigation showed that her suicidal attempts were really efforts to kill not only herself but also her parents, especially her mother and her husband with whom she identified, and introjected into, herself. Moreover, the patient's depressions were always followed by a state of euphoria of the hypomanic type, during which the superego or conscience quieted down, and the ego, as it were, rehabilitated itself; the patient then showed a pressure activity in her social affairs and a pronounced oniomania. She busied herself either with social affairs or in shopping for clothes and jewelry. During this manic state, she was sometimes quite euphoric and repeated that she never felt better in her life. As the superego is a precipitate of all the prohibitions and inhibitions that were originally inculcated into us by our parents, especially by the father, we can say that the manic state which is a reaction to the melancholia signified that the patient was now, as it were, at peace with her father. In brief, the superego or conscience, which constitutes the highest mental evolution of modern man, manifests itself as a rigid and inexorable critic in some mental disturbances, especially in the so-called narcistic neuroses.

In his effort to trace the origin of the superego, Professor Freud compares the feeling of moral conscience with the sexual feelings that appear with the beginning of life,[5] whereas conscience does not show itself until much later. No child is born moral. Morality is acquired later as a result of external forces which come primarily from the parents. These influences are impressed on the child through love or through its deprivation, for, being helpless and dependent, the child dreads nothing more than the loss of parental love, which it perceives as *real anxiety*. But the ultimate step in the formation of the superego does not occur until the child identifies himself with the father. At about the age of four to five, as a result of a real castration threat, the boy usually abandons the mother as a direct love object and represses her into his unconscious. That having been accomplished, the rivalry between him and his father ceases, and he then disposes of his father by assimilating him or by identifying himself with him. Henceforth, all the interdictions and commands that emanated from the father, or rather from the parents, are turned inside and form the superego or conscience. Instead of the former outer influences and authority, the individual is now guided by the same feelings from within. This transformation, as we said, is a process of identification, or an assimilation by the ego of a strange or foreign ego, as a result of which the child later behaves in certain situations like the parents. Professor Freud compares this process to an oral cannibalistic incorporation of a strange person; for the underlying thought of cannibalism was really an incorporation of the attributes that were formerly possessed by the strong conquered enemy. The Christian communion has the same meaning and is undoubtedly of the same origin.[6]

Let us now see what relations the various strata of the psychic apparatus have to the dynamics of the origin of a neurosis. We

[5] *Three Contributions to the Theory of Sex*, p. 533.
[6] Cf. *Totem and Taboo*, in *The Basic Writings of Sigmund Freud*, p. 807, translated by A. A. Brill, Modern Library, 1938.

know that the forces that impel the id to action originate in the organs of the body and are expressions of the great physical needs. When the child is hungry or uncomfortable it cries for the mother. In later life these simple needs become more complex and constitute what the philosophers call the instincts of hunger and love. Fundamentally, however, they are the same in so far as they represent stimuli for psychic activity. The id is entirely swayed by these instincts, and when a part of it later becomes modified into an ego, that, too, is dominated by the same instinctive energy. If an individual is stimulated by hunger or sex, the result is a rise in tension which the organism strives to lower through gratification; that is, it strives to produce a situation in which the physical need, hunger or love, will be extinguished. For the organism perceives a diminution of tension as pleasurable and a rise of tension as painful, and the tendency is, therefore, to keep tension at a low level. Such fluctuations of tension result in a series of pleasure-pain feelings, which in a way regulate all the activities of the psychic apparatus.

However, the instinctive needs that originate in the id can be gratified only through the help of the ego which alone is in contact with the outer world. To express it more precisely, the motive power that puts the machinery into motion originates in the id, while the steering and control of it must be guided by the ego, without which gratification cannot attain its aim. Hence, when the instinctive needs strive for immediate relief, the ego, with the help of the sense organs of the system of consciousness, impedes and controls these impetuous impulses or "passions." Through the ego, gratifications may be postponed and cravings modified or even given up altogether. In brief, the ego tames the excitements emanating from the id, and in this way replaces the pleasure principles by the principle of reality. In a way, the ego pursues the same aims as the id, but by virtue of its knowledge of the outer world, it takes account of its lawfulness and regularity, and instead of permitting the id to run blindly into dangerous situations, the ego interposes reason between the desire and the act. In our psychoanalytic work we can plainly see the vehement conflicts that sometimes rage in the individual for a long period of time before they are settled in one way or another. Through the efforts of the ego, it sometimes happens that conditions in the outer world are changed before a particular gratification can be attained. The decision as to when it is more convenient to control one's passions and bow to reality, or when to take their part and take "arms against a sea of troubles," constitutes the essence of one's philosophy of life.[7]

Bearing in mind the functions of the three forces of the psychic apparatus, we can understand how a struggle between the ego, id, and superego can produce sufficient tension to upset the mental equilibrium, especially in a sensitive or neurotic personality. The nature of the tension we know is usually a feeling of guilt in some degree or form. The erotic element, which Freud stresses in the neuroses, is naturally not always present in the narrow sexual sense but in the broad sense of libido which we discussed above.

To illustrate the functions of these forces, let us cite the following case: A young woman had been treated for some time because of a painful arm which was finally diagnosed as hysterical. The symptom represented, as Freud would put it, a monument of a past frustrated sexual situation of which the patient was entirely unconscious. The arm was selected as the seat of the symptom because that organ would be least suspected of harboring any sex. The libidinal cathexis which was perceived as pain represented displaced energy from the part of the body below the waistline. The selection of the arm was also determined by the fact that at the time her lover pressed her arm, the patient experienced a definite feeling in her genitals, and as the sensation in the arm was the less culpable of the two, it was naturally preferred for the seat of the conversion symptom. For owing to her moral and religious nature, the ego when confronted with the sexual struggle could not possibly permit the instinctive id impulses any motor discharge. Instead the ego brought about a repression into the unconscious. If that had continued, the patient would have remained healthy, but the repressed material struggled against this fate and obtained for itself an outlet by devious paths over which the ego had no control. That is, the repression failed and the cathexis

[7] Freud: *Die Frage der Laienanalyse,* p. 35.

originally connected with the conflict came to the surface in disguised form, as a substitutive formation for the original primitive desire, and thus constituted the symptom of the psychoneurosis. In terms of the psychic forces, *the neurosis thus represented a struggle between the ego and the id.*

The situation in the psychosis represents a *struggle between the ego and the outer world,* as will be shown by the following case of paranoid schizophrenia: A middle-aged, unmarried woman complained that for many years a gang had persecuted her. They watched her, talked about her maliciously and annoyed her at night with electric machines by throwing electrical shocks all over her body, particularly into her legs. The patient repeated these delusions with monotonous regularity whenever questioned, but was otherwise altogether indifferent to her environment. According to the history, the malady began with an acute attack of excitement which gradually changed into a catatonic stupor from which she emerged after a number of months.

We know that a delusion represents a patch imposed on an erstwhile tear in the relation between the ego and the outer world, and judging by the whole morbid picture, of which only a small fragment is presented, we can say that as a result of a vehement struggle between the ego and the outer world, the ego tore itself away from the whole outer world. During the stuporous state, no perceptions from the outer world could influence the patient; she was entirely impervious to all outer impressions, and even later when she became slightly accessible, her interest in life was extremely narrow and dulled; even her delusional complaints seemed devoid of affectivity. From their content and from her previous history, we can surmise the nature of the original conflict. She was a very reserved and rigid old maid and became psychotic after an abortive love affair. A gang of men torturing her by throwing electricity into her body is usually a symbolic representation of a desire for sex and coitus.

The case of melancholia mentioned above illustrates the conflict in a narcistic neurosis, which represents a *struggle between the ego and the superego.* It is best seen in melancholias where the patient is usually very desirous of admitting his guilt and is not only willing to suffer condign punishment but not infrequently demands it. Usually the patient is suicidal and often attempts suicide unless the picture changes from the depressive to the manic phase. Let me, therefore, give here an abstract of Freud's theoretical concepts and then cite an illustrative case.

Proceeding from mourning to its pathologic counterpart, melancholia, Freud correlates the two and states that both are produced by the same exciting causes. Mourning is a reaction to the loss of a loved person, or to the loss of some abstraction that has taken the place of one, such as fatherland, liberty, or an ideal. The same process produces melancholia in those persons who are morbidly predisposed to it. The symptoms, which need not be enumerated here, are the same in both, except that self-depreciation, which is very marked in melancholia, is absent in mourning. The process of adjustment that takes place in the mourner is as follows: Once he is convinced that the loved object is lost, he strives consciously and unconsciously to withdraw his libido from the object. But as we are never willing to give up a libido position, he struggles against this inexorable need. In very sensitive persons or in neurotics, this may not be achieved; a reactive psychosis may sometimes develop and the loved object is then hallucinatorily retained. Thus, a young woman who lost her husband became schizophrenic and then imagined that her husband was alive, that she heard him talk in the next house or in the street. As time went on, she mistook the identity of people, and then thought that the hospital physician was her husband. This situation continued for more than thirty years until she died. In the average person, such withdrawal of libido eventually takes place, though it is often carried out slowly.

Melancholia, too, may be a reaction to the loss of a loved person although the object may not have died, as in the case of mourning, but have become lost as an object of love, as in the case of jilting. In some cases of melancholia, the patient feels a loss, but he cannot consciously perceive what he has really lost; that is, the patient knows whom he has lost, but not *what* he has lost in that object. In contradistinction to mourning, in which there is nothing unconscious about the loss, melancholia is in some way related to an unconscious loss. In grief, the ego's state of inhibition and loss of interest are due to the active work of mourning; in melancholia, the unknown love results in an inner labor of the same kind and produces the well-known retardation or inhibition of melancholia. In melancholia, there is also a marked self-depreciation, an impoverishment of the ego which is absent in grief. The melancholiac considers his ego, his self, as worthless, and even contemptible; he blames himself for all sorts of commissions and omissions which go back to his remote past, and he invariably feels that he should be punished for them.

Freud asserts that it is fruitless, scientifically and therapeutically, to contradict patients who hurl such accusations against their own ego. The patient must be right in some way; he describes something that surely corresponds to what he thinks. It is also noteworthy that in contrast to the mourner, the melancholiac seems to lack a sense of shame; he obviously takes pleasure in exposing himself as the worst villain or sinner and acts as if he had lost his self-respect. One part of his ego criticizes the other, as it were, and looks upon it as if it were a separate object. Freud continues: "Our suspicion is that this critical force which is here split off from the ego will also prove its independence in other circumstances, and will be confirmed by all other observations. We shall really find cause for separating this force from the rest of the ego." [8]

As I said above, Freud calls this mental faculty *conscience*, and in conjunction with conscious censorship and the testing of reality, it belongs to the great institutions of the ego. Somewhere we shall also find evidence that it alone can become sick. For if one listens patiently to the many self-accusations of melancholiacs, it becomes impossible to dismiss the feeling that the most potent of them are hardly applicable to the patient but that with slight modifications they fit someone else, some person whom the patient loves, has loved, or should love. Thus the key to the morbid picture consists in recognizing that the patient's self-reproaches are really reproaches against a loved object and that these reproaches have been rolled onto the patient's own ego. For example, one of my patients repeatedly accused herself of murder by reiterating in a

[8] "Trauer und Melancholie," *Internat. Ztschr. f. ärztl. Psychoanal.*, IV, 292.

stereotyped manner: "Yes, I will be electrocuted for murder; why did you save me? I am a murderer." After the attack subsided, I discovered that the patient had harbored deep suspicions that her mother had actually poisoned her father, and the accusations of murder were really hurled against her mother with whom she had identified herself. Another melancholic woman disparaged herself as being weak-minded and dishonest, characteristics in no way fitting her own personality. Investigation later showed that her husband actually had been very inferior to her and that he had been involved in several fraudulent transactions. Indeed, it is because everything depreciatory which such patients hurl on themselves really belongs to someone else that they are not ashamed to express these sometimes horrific accusations.

Bearing this in mind, the situation can now be reconstructed as follows: There was an attachment of libido to some particular person, such as a parent or an outside loved object, when, as a result of some real vexation or disappointment emanating from the loved person, this object relation was shaken. Normally such a trauma would have resulted in a withdrawal of libido from this object and a displacement of it to a new object. Here, however, the object cathexis proved to be only slightly resistant, and was, therefore, abandoned; but the free libido, instead of being transferred to another object, was drawn back to the ego. There it served to establish an *identification* of the ego with the abandoned object. Thus, "The shadow of the object fell upon the ego, which henceforth could be criticized by a special mental force as if it were an object, like the lost object. In this way, the loss of the object became transformed into a loss in the ego, and the conflict between the ego and the loved person became transformed into a dispute between the criticizing ego and the part of the ego which was changed by the identification." [9]

Mrs. C., aged forty-nine, a widow, was brought to me about four years ago by her brother, a physician, who assured me that there was nothing organically wrong with her but that about a week before she had attempted suicide by gas inhalation. As is usual with relatives, he tried to belittle her suicidal attempt by saying that she

[9] *Ibid.*, p. 293.

really did not mean to kill herself. He thought that her depression was due to the change of life. When I suggested that she probably had had similar depressions before, the patient related that at the age of eighteen she had been nervous for about five months and at the time had been quite depressed and thought of suicide. Eight years ago, following her husband's death, she went through another depression which lasted many months. There was no doubt that she was a typical case of manic-depressive psychosis.

Her brother stressed the peculiar nature of her depression which was centered in the following episode: Her son (who was her favorite child) was in love with a young woman, the daughter of one of her friends, and he told his mother that he wished to marry her. The patient, who was hitherto quite uncommunicative, then continued the story, saying that although she had always approved of this young lady, she thought that her son was too young to marry, especially since he was still studying law. She said emphatically: "Doctor, I did not want him to give her up; I just wanted him to postpone the marriage." However, in order to impress him, she told him that the girl was too young and too impulsive, and insinuated that she could not be trusted. The patient repeated that whatever she told her son about the girl was absolutely true and repeated: "When I said she could not be trusted, I did not mean anything bad; the girl is a good girl, but I must have exaggerated it by the way I said it, because about a month later, he broke his engagement to her." The patient was extremely upset when she heard this, protesting that she did not mean to do any harm to an innocent girl. She could not, however, stop talking about it, and became increasingly depressed and agitated because she was sure the girl would commit suicide.

Her brother then took up the conversation and said that the son repeatedly assured his mother that she was wrong, that he did not misinterpret her statement, and that she had very little, if anything, to do with his change of heart. Yet despite repeated assurances by her son and others, the patient was obsessed by the feeling that the young woman would commit suicide, and this finally drove her to a suicidal attempt. Her brother added that, from his own investigation, the young woman in question was not at all depressed over the broken engagement, and that she was already keeping company with a new admirer. The patient nevertheless remained inexorable and would not listen to these assurances; she was sure that the young lady would commit suicide and that it was her fault for maligning an innocent girl.

Here one could clearly see the struggle between the ego and the superego. The patient felt guilty for driving an innocent girl to her grave, and by the *lex talionis* she herself deserved death and her conscience thus drove her into an attempt at self-annihilation. Looking at the case superficially, one would say that the patient's feelings and views were entirely unjustified, that her whole behavior was most illogical in the face of facts. However, as Freud pointed out, it was futile to remonstrate with her; she felt sure that she was right, and for us it was simply a question of finding the key to the disharmony between the *noopsyche* and the *thymopsyche*. The accent surely did not belong where the patient placed it. She attempted and still wished to commit suicide because she drove "an innocent girl into suicide," though the girl in reality was now well adjusted to the situation and the patient repeatedly assured of it. Her behavior clearly represented a distortion of the real situation brought about by the mechanisms of displacement and substitution of the ideational content, but the affects, the feelings, she displayed were undoubtedly true. In other words, the depression was justified; she felt it and tried hard to rationalize it. Such mechanisms are quite common not only in symptoms but also in dreams and wit.[10]

I would be pleased if I could give all the findings of this interesting case, but since it is not possible I shall present a few of the salient points, enough to explain some of its unconscious mechanisms. The relation between mother and son had always been very close and in the analysis I found that the patient invariably disliked and hated every girl who aroused his interest. In this case she was, however, quite careful not to show her resentment as continuously as she was wont to do on similar occasions, probably because she was on friendly terms with the girl's parents and because her son reacted very strongly against her first remarks.

[10] *The Interpretation of Dreams* in *Freud's Basic Writings,* p. 434.

Thereafter, she was careful, but what she said was emphatic; she usually added: "I don't wish to quarrel with you, the girl is very nice, but . . ." Moreover, this was not the first time she had interfered with her son's desire for marriage. Whenever he showed any serious intentions of marrying, she immediately found a way of stopping it.

When I investigated the causes of her former depressions I found that the last one—following her husband's death—expressed itself in feelings of guilt about her husband. He would have lived if she had done this or that—trifles—which covered up represssed hostile wishes against him. In discussing her relations to her husband, the associations led to the man who was the center of her first depression and this really furnished the key to the distortions of her present attack.

Her first depression occurred at about the age of eighteen following a short but impressive amour with a married man which left her with a strong sense of guilt. She had every reason to distrust the man; she heard and saw much of his reckless behavior, yet she allowed herself to be seduced by him. For some unexplainable reason he then abruptly broke all relations with her. She naturally became deeply depressed; she also feared pregnancy and thought seriously of killing herself even after she was convinced to the contrary. It was particularly difficult for her to get over the affair because she was forced to see the man daily while at work. She was also sure that another woman employed in the same department maligned her and had alienated him from her. For many months she had thought seriously of killing him, her rival, and herself. However, she gradually gained full control of herself and for a few months felt quite well. I had no doubt that the depression then turned into a hypomanic state. If we now correlate the factors of the first depression with Freud's concepts as given above (see p. 160) we can then understand her peculiar expressions and behavior.

Briefly, her son's love affair unconsciously aroused her long-forgotten and painful affair, with all its concomitant affects, and she then accused her son's fiancée of her own former misdeeds. It recalls the story of the man who asked his friend why his wife was so jealous of his secretary and the answer: "She was my secretary long before we thought of marrying." In other words, the patient identified her son with her first lover and herself with his fiancée, and whereas her incest barrier precluded any sexual ideas about her son, she could freely indulge in sexual fantasies regarding him and the girl. And as she had blamed herself for her first sexual transgression and wished at that time to commit murder and suicide, she now unconsciously transferred this situation to her son and the girl. During the analysis it was revealed that she told her son that she had heard some bad rumors about the girl and that therefore he could not trust her. Throughout the depression, she had entirely forgotten the first part of this compound sentence, which was undoubtedly due to the fact that what she attributed to the girl was based on her own repressed history. When her son angrily demanded that she tell him the source of the rumors, she became excited and ran out of the room saying: "I don't wish to quarrel with you; the girl is very nice, but . . ." Her repetitions that the girl was nice was only an effort at self-defense.

In other words, she identified the girl with herself as well as with her first hated rival. The loss of the old love object which was so painful during her first depression was now transferred to the fear of losing her son. The average mother not infrequently feels some pangs when her son abandons her for another woman who can offer him everything the mother gave plus sexual union. Some mothers never entirely resign themselves to their lot and become bad mothers-in-law. But as a rule the mother distributes such floating libido to other children or somehow sublimates it. Here, that was not quite possible; it concerned her favorite son who for years had been her greatest outlet, and as soon as there was a threat of losing him, it unconsciously aroused a situation that is entirely foreign in ordinary life. All the dormant ghosts were revived. She was again in the midst of her first experience when she lost the beloved object in such a strange way. The new images and feelings were quickly added to the old ones and the shadows of the old objects—first lover, husband—were revived in her ego (identification) and she was then able to criticize herself in the same manner as she criticized her seducer and her husband.

I cannot give here a full history of her relations to her husband except to say that their premarital experiences resembled in many respects those of her first love affair; they simply turned out differently. Much of this past history returned unconsciously in the depression after her husband died, and that was the reason for blaming herself for his untimely death. In the last episode she identified her son's fiancée with her first rival whom she thought of killing, and the obsessive thought that she would commit suicide emanated from that unconscious wish. In other words, in her suicidal attempt she really wished to kill the old lost object, the first seducer, the first rival, her husband, her son, and his fiancée. As Freud puts it: "The ego can kill itself only after the return to it of the object cathexis, when it can treat itself as an object, when it can direct that hostility against itself, which belongs to another object, and which represents that primary reaction of the ego to the outer world." [11] Or, as he expressed it more explicitly, "Probably no one has the mental energy required to kill himself unless in the first place he is, in doing this, at the same time killing an object with whom he has identified himself, and in the second place, is turning against himself a death wish which had been directed against someone else." [12]

The conditions necessary to produce such a process are, first, a strong fixation on the love object and, second, which is contradictory to this, a slightly resistive object cathexis. It was Otto Rank who gave the explanation for this contradiction; he said that the object selection is here effected on a narcistic background and, therefore, when the object cathexis encounters any difficulties, it can then regress to narcism. The narcistic identification with the object then takes the place of the love cathexis, with the result that despite the conflict with the beloved person, affectionate relations can still continue. Such a situation brings to mind cases we frequently encounter in everyday life and in practice. Husbands and wives are forever fighting and now and then haling each other to courts and to psychiatrists. But woe betide him who tries to

[11] *Trauer und Melancholie,* p. 295.
[12] "Über die Psychogenese eines Falles von weiblicher Homosexualität," *Gesammelte Schriften,* V, 331.

remove the psychopathic husband by having him arrested for his brutality to his wife or by sending him to an institution. Every experienced psychiatrist has learned to steer clear of such cases, for the contending partners then forget their own mutual hatreds and turn them on the physician or on the innocent good Samaritan. Such a process naturally corresponds to the *regression* of one type of object choice to the original narcism. But it has already been shown that identification is the primal stage of object selection, that it represents the first ambivalent expression of how the ego behaves to an object. It would like to incorporate this object, by way of the oral or cannibalistic phase of libido development, by devouring it. Abraham justly traces to it the refusal of nourishment in deep states of melancholia. This mechanism is glaringly seen in cases I have designated as "psychic suicide," [13] that is, people in whom the wish to die is achieved without resorting to any physical agent. This phenomenon of "dying at will" has been frequently observed among primitive races, and I have shown that it occurs also in some enlightened people in our own times. But unlike the process of melancholia which produces a turmoil in the environment, the struggle that brings about psychic suicide as a rule proceeds silently, altogether endopsychically. The exception to this rule is "anorexia nervosa" which some mild or incipient schizophrenics, frequently diagnosed as hysterics, utilize as a mode of committing suicide. Although they produce some disturbance in their immediate environment by their refusal to eat and by vomiting, they show neither the picture of melancholia nor the acute course of psychic suicide. Descriptively they fit into Stekel's designation of "chronic suicide," despite the fact that most of them do not die.[14]

Freud admits that this concept—which places the predisposition to melancholia, or a part of it, under the dominance of the narcistic type of object choice—still requires further confirmation. Nevertheless, he does not hesitate to assume among the special character-

[13] "The Concept of Psychic Suicide," *Internat. J. Psycho-Anal.*, vol. XX, 1939.
[14] The writer is at present preparing the manuscript for a volume on "Psychic Suicide."

istics of melancholia a regression from object cathexis to the oral phase of libido which still belongs to narcism. Such identification lies in the object cathexis, which is given up in hysteria, whereas in melancholia it persists and manifests itself in some individual actions and innervations.

TEN

MOURNING, MELANCHOLIA, AND COMPULSIONS

As A general outline of this narcistic neurosis (as Freud designates it because it represents a regression to the earliest phase of narcism, namely, the oral phase), it will suffice to show the marked consistency of Freud's general approach to the problem of the neuroses and psychoses. The excellence of all his contributions lies in the fact that he always started with the symptom and gradually wound his way through the abnormal processes, through the maze of the unconscious, straight back to its normal counterpart. No one before him had the daring and ingenuity to do anything like it. In this puzzling psychosis he showed that melancholia, like grief, is a reaction—to be sure, an exaggerated one—to a loss of a love object which invariably offers a good opportunity to render prominently the ambivalence that always exists in love affairs. This ambivalence invests the conflict of grief with a pathologic configuration wherever there is a predisposition to compulsion neurosis. The patient then feels that he is responsible for the death of the love object and reproaches himself for it. Such compulsive states of depressions plainly show what the conflict of ambivalence alone can do without the regressive withdrawal of libido.

The causes of melancholia extend mostly beyond the clear sense of a loss through death and include all those situations of aggravation, depreciation, and disappointment that bring into the relation a contrast between love and hatred or reinforce an existent ambivalence. If the love for the object, which cannot be given up, takes refuge in narcistic identification while the object itself is given up, then hate takes possession of this substitutive object by insulting, depreciating, and causing it to suffer, and thus obtains a sadistic gratification from it. The self-torture of melancholiacs, which is undoubtedly pleasurable, has the same meaning as in the corresponding phenomena of compulsion neurosis. It is a gratification of sadistic and hate tendencies which belong to an object but which have been turned on one's own person. In both affections, the patients usually succeed in taking revenge on the original objects by the devious path of self-punishment. They torment them by means of their illness which they have developed in order not to be forced to show directly their hostility. Thus the erotic cathexis of the melancholiac's object undergoes a twofold fate: part of it regresses to the object and another part, under the influence of the ambivalent conflict, is put back to its nearer stage of sadism.

It is this sadism which explains the tendency to self-destruction which is so dangerous in melancholia. But since the self-love of the ego is so vast that an enormous amount of narcistic libido is freed whenever there is a threat to life, we cannot conceive that this ego can destroy itself. Hence, we must conclude that no neurotic can entertain suicidal thoughts which are not murderous impulses against others which he turned back upon himself.

Having demonstrated the resemblances of melancholia to compulsion neurosis in so far as its regression to sadism is concerned, Freud then explains some of the striking features of melancholia. Thus, the *delusion of poverty* so often encountered in this disease is nothing but anal-erotism, torn out of its context and changed by regression. The *insomnia*, another characteristic feature of melancholia, points to the rigidity of the condition, that is, the impossibility of carrying out the general drawing in of the libido necessary for sleep. The melancholic complex behaves like an open wound by drawing to itself cathetic energies from all sides (the counter-cathexis in the transference neurosis) and thus draining the ego to complete depletion. It thus can easily resist the ego's wish to sleep. Freud thinks that the *improvement depressed patients show toward evening* is probably due to some somatic condition and is not to be explained psychologically.

But the most remarkable peculiarity of melancholia and one that requires the most explanation is *its tendency to become transformed into the symptomatically opposite state of mania.* We know that not all melancholic depressions follow this course; many show intervals during which no signs of mania can be observed.

On the other hand, some show regular alternations of depressed and manic phases and these have been designated as circular, or cyclothymic, insanities.

Freud thinks that it is incumbent upon us to extend the analytic explanation of melancholia to mania and he mentions two starting points to this approach. The first is the analytic viewpoint, and the second is based on general economic experience. The psycho-analytic viewpoint states that several investigators have already shown that the content of mania is no different from that of melancholia, that both are struggling with some "complex" to which the ego succumbs in melancholia, whereas in mania it masters the "complex" or shoves it aside. The other point is based on the experience that all states of pleasure, jubilance and triumph, which show the normal picture of mania, present the same economic condition. In all of them we deal with an activity that sets free a large amount of psychic expenditure that had existed for a long time or had been established through force of habit, so that it can now be manifoldly used for all possible discharges. Thus it is when a poor devil is suddenly relieved of the chronic worriment about his daily bread by suddenly winning a large sum of money, or when a long and hard struggle is finally crowned with success, or when one finds oneself in a position to give up an oppressive burden or some false position. All such situations are characterized by an elated feeling or by signs of discharge of a pleasurable affect, and it is this enhanced readiness to enter into all kinds of activities which recalls mania in contrast to the depression and retardation of melancholia. Freud ventures to say that *mania is nothing but such a triumph, except that the ego does not know what it has conquered or over what it has triumphed.*

Alcohol may produce a similar state of mind which is probably due to a letdown in repression expenditure which, in turn, is probably due to the toxin. The layman readily assumes that the continuous motion pleasure and the marked desire to take up new things seen in such maniacal states are the results of "feeling well," but this is a false deduction. The euphoria and the uninhibited activity are really due to the fulfillment of the above-mentioned economic condition in the psychic life. In brief, in mania the ego surmounts the loss of the object (or the mourning over the loss or perhaps the object itself) which then frees for other uses the whole sum of counter-cathexis which the painful suffering of melancholia drew from the ego and bound to itself. The manic also demonstrates to us clearly his liberation from the object that tormented him by his feverish pursuit of a new object cathexis.

An example of this is the case of a man of thirty-five who had lost his newly wed bride in an automobile accident two weeks after marriage. He was a timid and reserved person who, prior to the marriage, had had no relations of any kind with the opposite sex. His behavior toward his wife, whom he had known for about twenty years, had been purely platonic up until a few months before marriage. This was because, owing to religious differences, his parents had objected to his marrying her; and although he himself was sure that he would marry her some day, he nevertheless refrained from any close relations with her. In brief, we dealt with a schizoid personality. Following the tragedy the patient was somewhat depressed for more than six months, during which time he expressed suicidal thoughts. At the end of this period, he merged into a mild euphoric state in which his attitude to women was entirely changed. In contrast to his former reserved behavior, he now made advances to women whenever an opportunity presented itself. His cousin brought him to me, thinking there was something wrong with him because he was entangled with four women, each of whom he promised to marry. My investigations disclosed that every one of these women represented some physical or mental trait of his dead wife, and that besides these four women, he had pursued many others. The patient's reason for his changed behavior was that he really did not know what he was doing. It recalls the joke about the man who was missed when his wife's funeral procession was about to start. His brother-in-law, who was looking for him, finally found him making love to the maid. He reproached him by saying that he was amazed at his behavior, particularly on such occasion; to which the bereaved husband replied: "On such occasion, does one know what one is doing?"

Ordinarily we laugh at this answer because we are surprised at such incompatible behavior. If we analyze the witticism, we say that it represents what the Germans call *Galgen-humor* (humor of the gallows) or "grim humor." Humor enables us to gain pleasure despite a painful situation. When we hear that the funeral procession is about to start we naturally empathize ourselves with the poor bereaved husband and feel his great grief, but the depressing emotion disappears as soon as we hear of his paradoxical behavior and his naïve reply: one does not know what one does on such occasion. We not only cease sympathizing with him but our depression changes into pleasure and laughter. The pleasure was here produced at the cost of the discontinued liberation of the painful feeling, or through the *economized expenditure of affect*.[1] In terms of the forces of the psychic apparatus, we can say that the ego refuses to be downed by reality. After suffering reaches a certain height, the ego rebels against it and either ignores the trauma altogether or belittles it. Our patient, who became involved in so many amorous situations regardless of reality and contrary to his own former behavior, acted like the husband in the joke. He could not stand the mounting pain from the loss of his love object, and his ego therefore wiped out, as it were, the whole trauma so that he could then strive to replenish his loss through other love objects. Again like the husband in the joke, his actions seemed to say: "The death of a wife is not as terrible as conventional morality makes believe. For after all she can readily be replaced by other women."

This kind of emotional reversal takes place in the turning from melancholia to mania and in other psychopathological behavior.[2] In everyday life, we often observe a person who has been deprived of a love object soon attaching himself to a new one and marrying on the rebound. In the manic state, which follows as a reaction to the depression, the patient's behavior often manifests itself in a series of rebounds. Our patient acted as if none of these women really could take the place of his lost wife. He thus ran unceasingly from one to the other. As a matter of fact, analysis showed that

---

[1] Freud: *Wit and Its Relation to the Unconscious*, in *Freud's Basic Writings*, p. 798.

[2] Brill: "The Mechanism of Wit and Humor in Normal and Psychopathic States," *Psychiatric Quart.*, October, 1940.

had his wife lived he would have probably left her in a short time for he was unconsciously fixed on his mother. He could marry this particular woman because she was so different from his mother that she could in no way recall her to him. In brief, it was a so-called exogamous marriage which we know does not as a rule last very long.

At all events, his feverish effort to attach himself to so many women showed a manic's desire for a new object cathexis.

It is not always easy to demonstrate all these mechanisms, but now and then we encounter a neurotic situation that shows all these intricacies with surprising clearness. The following case gives a glimpse of how some of these forces vie with each other.

Miss G., a cultured girl of twenty-five, had suffered from compulsion neurosis (doubts, phobias, and obsessions) since the age of seven or eight. I considered her more than a mere neurotic for she sometimes had mild depressions and ideas of reference which made the diagnosis and prognosis rather doubtful. The symptoms were of an anal-sadistic nature. She was constantly afraid of contamination, especially through contact with her mother and father, more particularly the former. Thus all dishes had to be passed to her at the table before they could be offered to her mother, because otherwise the whole platter was contaminated. She went through many ceremonials daily, some of them lasting for hours, during which she obsessively washed her hands or cleansed some other part of her body. Her family had to put a cross on a sort of chart that hung in the bathroom, giving the exact time each of them used the bathroom. She had to know this because she could not use the room for at least half an hour thereafter. She claimed that the odor left there was contaminating and disagreeable and that it took half an hour before it was dissipated. Sadism colored all her thoughts and actions, indirectly through unconscious manifestations as well as openly. She was fascinated by sadistic fantasies and literature, loved dramas and doted on murder cases. After treating her regularly for about a year with some success, the following episode occurred. One morning, the patient joyously reported by telephone that all her symptoms had suddenly disappeared, that she now felt fine and therefore wished to stop the analysis. This euphoric feeling continued for two days, but on the morning of the third day all the symptoms had reappeared.

It sometimes happens that a patient suddenly shows a marked improvement, particularly at the beginning of psychoanalytic treatment, which can usually be attributed to the state of transference; sometimes a conversion hysterical symptom quickly disappears following its abreaction. But it was the first time in my experience that a compulsive neurotic suddenly felt entirely freed of all symptoms. I was somewhat puzzled, but under no illusions about the permanence of this recovery and was, therefore, not a bit surprised when she telephoned on the morning of the third day to say that all the symptoms had returned.

Investigation showed that all the symptoms disappeared on the morning following the electrocution of Ruth Snyder and Judd Gray for the murder of the former's husband, Albert. The patient was extremely absorbed in this murder case which had been in the newspaper headlines for months. Her sadistic impulses found a ready outlet in reading about it and attending the trial. On the day of execution, January 13, 1928, the patient fasted the whole day and spent hours weeping. For reasons unexplainable to her, she sympathized with the murderess although she considered her guilty and even feared lest she be pardoned. Analysis showed that she identified herself with Ruth Snyder and lived through with her the murder and the trial as well as the expiation. The whole murder case offered her an excellent medium for emotional catharsis, for she had a very strong need for punishment by virtue of her own hostile wishes to both parents, especially to the mother. In other words, the patient lived through, in miniature, a manic-depressive attack. She was agitated and depressed during the trial which dragged on for months, and her interest in the case was kept alive from the end of May when the death sentence was pronounced until it was carried out about eight months later, culminating in fasting and mourning during the day of execution. But the following morning she felt entirely freed of all her symptoms; her depression had changed into a hypomanic euphoria which lasted a few days.

It would be impossible to explain this episode without a knowledge of the contending psychic forces as described by Freud in his scheme of the psychic apparatus mentioned above (see p. 151). The patient, as we said, was on a pregenital level with narcistic fixations in the anal and oral phases of libido development. During the analysis I noted that she showed distinct emotional fluctuations of depression and elation, but as the obsessive symptoms dominated the whole picture, I naturally paid little attention to anything else. It was only after witnessing the short depressive-manic episode that I paid attention to her emotional fluctuations and then definitely called her a schizoid-manic showing a preponderating picture of compulsion neurosis with regular emotional fluctuations of varying intensity.[3]

Without delving into the deeper structures of the case, I wish to say that the patient was an extremely narcistic personality who demonstrated practically all the mechanisms described by Freud as characteristic of depressions and elations, as well as those of compulsion neurosis. In identifying herself with the murderess who was executed for her crime, the patient went through the same phases as the ordinary melancholiac who finally attempts or actually commits suicide. But as every experienced psychiatrist knows, following such an unsuccessful attempt the patient is usually glad to be alive and his depressive symptoms not only disappear but he may even become euphoric. In this case, there was never any thought of suicide, yet the patient vicariously went through an electrocution through which she atoned for those sins which tormented her during the months of the trial and subsequent imprisonment of Ruth Snyder. In terms of the narcistic neurosis, the ego accepted the extreme punishment from the superego and having paid the penalty was now free and no longer feared the superego. That accounts for the change of mood from depression to elation which in our patient showed itself in a complete freedom from symptoms and in a euphoric mood, lasting, however, only two days. For as she was preponderatingly a compulsive neurotic, the obsessive acts of counting, touching, and washing, which only represented efforts to mitigate the need for punishment emanating

[3] This case was reported in my paper, "The Application of Psychoanalysis to Psychiatry," *J. Nerv. and Ment. Dis.*, December, 1928.

from the superego, could not be kept long in abeyance. For the same situation that produced her neurosis and kept it alive was still there. On the other hand, a pure case of melancholia following a suicidal attempt, whether he merges into an elation or not, invariably goes through a long remission during which he is entirely free from symptoms. Such emotional fluctuations as described in Miss G. and similar cases show a marked resemblance to such well-known religious ceremonials as the Jewish Day of Atonement, which is preceded by a period of quasi-depression, characterized by praying and fasting, and followed by a joyous holiday. Witness, also, the medieval dedication of churches, wherein riotous license was followed by extreme repentance and expiation.

The superego, as we have already said, is most intimately connected with the fate of the Oedipus complex which Freud considers to be the nucleus of all future individual adjustment.[4] When the Oedipus complex becomes resolved and disappears, the superego takes its place. All the important emotional attachments of childhood are taken over by the superego and are gradually consolidated for adult behavior. As time goes on, other identifications, other precipitates, take place in the ego, but it is only the first, that of the father, which produces a transformation of a special kind. The superego is actually the representative of all moral restrictions, of all ideal perfections. It is not only a precipitate of the parents, but of the parents' parents, as well as of their substitutes, for example, teachers. It is, in fine, the bearer of the traditions and cultural assets of the past generations. But these attributes preponderate mainly in the male sex, whose Oedipus complex comes to an end at a very early age as a result of a castration threat. The feminine sex, whose narcism does not really begin to flourish before puberty, never evinces the unyielding characteristics of the superego formation. It is for this reason that women have always been so responsive to emotional innovations.[5]

In the deeper-reaching psychotic disturbances, the ego's tendencies and struggles are not so clearly discernible as in the com-

---

[4] *The Interpretation of Dreams,* in *Freud's Basic Writings,* p. 306.
[5] *New Introductory Lectures,* p. 176, New York, W. W. Norton and Co.

pulsive neurotics, but they are none the less always present and active, as is shown by the following case.

About four years ago I was consulted about Mrs. N., a married woman of fifty-four, who was subject to periodic attacks which had been repeatedly diagnosed by my predecessors as manic-depressive, and by me as schizoid-manic episodes. She had shown such clear-cut attacks since the age of sixteen. For the past fifteen years it had usually been necessary to keep her in a hospital during the attacks. Apparently without any reason, the patient would become depressed, resistive, irritable, and soon very active. Sometimes she answered questions, but usually she refused to talk or eat. She would go without food for days, until she had to be tube-fed; on some occasions she suddenly took a meal or two and stopped again. She showed very marked pressure activity which took the form of washing and cleaning the house for days and nights at a time; this was very marked when the disease was fully established. For the past ten years she had been living in a hotel, but that made little difference in her behavior. When the pressure activity came, she seized the brushes and pails from the chamber-maid and proceeded with the cleaning. There were many other symptoms, such as attacks of nausea and vomiting, and at times a strong desire for alcohol. The attacks lasted from a few months to a little over a year and usually ended suddenly. The patient apparently made a good recovery; there was no residuum of any kind to be noticed.

The patient had been under my care for more than four years, during which time she had six mild attacks, five of them needing no hospital treatment. The fourth occurred while I was abroad and her family thought it best to keep her in the hospital during my absence. In addition to the behavior mentioned, the patient also reacted to ideas of reference, had hallucinations, and evinced vague persecutory trends. At the height of the attack she imagined that men and occasionally women were spitting when they passed by; they made derogatory remarks about her, and she was even threatened with jail.

The patient was an only daughter of a dipsomaniacal army officer (probably of the manic-depressive type) who when sober was very affectionate, but brutal when under the influence of alcohol. Her older brother died when the patient was eight years old, and her mother died when she was nine years old, after which her paternal grandmother acted as mother to her. At the age of fifteen years she had sexual relations with a soldier who was her father's orderly. At nineteen she married a man eleven years her senior, who has always been very devoted and attentive to her. She had four children, all of whom are well and three of whom are happily married.

When the patient was thirty-seven years old, a dentist, she claims, attacked her sexually while treating her. She maintains that her more severe attacks date from that period. Investigation, however, showed that her attacks did not begin as suddenly as she imagined. She was always of a syntonic nature and subject to moods from early girlhood. The attacks were usually ushered in by a nightmare, in which odors—being suffocated by gas—played a part, or a depressive mood gradually settled on her. She soon felt unworthy and suicidal and began to worry over her past transgressions—especially over the adultery, as she called it.

Analysis showed that her attacks were in the nature of celebrations and atonements for her sins. Thus when her family asked her, after an attack, why she refused to eat, she usually said: "I am too fat; I may as well lose some flesh." But to me she first said that she had no appetite, that she despised food. Later it was demonstrated that the depression represented an atonement for her sins and that her refusal of nourishment was really a part of a suicidal attempt. She told her family that her pressure activity, in the form of cleaning, was an effort to keep herself busy and that the apartment really needed a good cleansing; but analysis showed that it was a symbolic cleansing—she was trying hard to wash away her sins. The disparaging remarks and signs all referred to some details of her forbidden acts. Thus the spitting referred to fellatio with the soldier, and putting the hand toward the mouth, which people did everywhere, referred to the episode with the dentist. The feeling of unworthiness and her suicidal attempts were the results of her guilty conscience. She admitted that she was a terrible person, deserving death, and was anxious to die.

I said that the patient was under my care for more than four years, but she received actual analysis for a period of only about six months. The patient lived in the South and could not remain in New York very long; something always happened to interrupt the analysis. However, she, as well as her family, was pleased with the results of the treatment.

I selected this case because it clearly demonstrates Abraham's views of the psychogenesis of a melancholic depression.[6] Abraham maintains that in all melancholic depressions one finds (1) a constitutional enhancement of the oral erotism which thus makes it possible to produce (2) a special fixation of libido on this zone, (3) a severe trauma to the infantile narcism through a combination of love disappointments, (4) the appearance of the first big love disappointment before the successful conquest of the Oedipus wishes, and (5) a repetition of the primary disappointment in later life, which gives cause for the onset of the melancholic depression.

The constitutional enhancement of the mouth erotism can be readily seen when you hear that the father and grandfather and many other members of the paternal side of the family were chronic alcoholics. There were also a number of stutterers on both sides of the family. The patient herself showed a marked oral erotism in her abnormal love for food and candy, in her periodic craving for alcohol, particularly following the depression, in her lifelong gastrointestinal troubles, in her dental difficulties which invariably determined her attacks,[7] and last, but not least, in a direct erogenous significance of the mouth, which showed itself in perverse kissing. Although she was genitally frigid, she could always get an orgasm through kissing and fellatio. The patient was preponderatingly pregenital; her object-libido output was extremely low. Her experiences with the soldier were perverse in character. She married because she was lonesome and hated to remain longer with her father, and although she was very fond of

[6] *Versuch einer Entwicklungsgeschichte der Libido*, p. 46, Internat. Psychoanalyt. Verlag, Wien, 1924. See translation in *Selected Papers of Karl Abraham*, London, Hogarth Press.

[7] Analysis showed that she was a willing victim, to say the least, in the assault episode. She continued her visits to this dentist for many years.

her husband, she was more or less objective about her married life.

In her symptoms one could readily discern a marked preponderance of hostility and rage (suicides, etc.) which could be traced to definite disappointments as a result of deprivations sustained from both parents. Her feeling toward her father was ambivalent. At the beginning of her life he was at times very affectionate, but when he was drunk, everybody was afraid of him. He often spanked her as a child, and her conscious hatred of him was traced to such an episode at a very early age (three or four). The odors in her dreams could always be traced to her father's smell of alcohol; her refusal to talk and eat was a rejection of the father, while her craving for alcohol, following the depression, was a reconciliation or an effort to incorporate him into herself through the mechanism of introjection. As a little girl she was extremely jealous of her older brother who was her mother's favorite. She repeatedly recalled the hostile wishes and hatred that she entertained toward him. His death, when she was eight, caused self-reproach which later played some part in her depressions. She blamed herself for it (omnipotence of thought). As a result of her early disagreeable experiences with her father, the Oedipus situation forever remained associated with her oral-sadistic impulses. Even when she was free from the attacks, she was always troubled by bad teeth (cannibalistic regression).

Analysis showed that the dentist was a direct father substitute and, following the sexual episode, that he always played a part in the attacks. She hated him because he did not cure her and also because of the assault which she associated with her father's spanking. During the attacks her early oral fantasies were repeated in her refusal to eat, and this was always associated with her erstwhile refusal of the mother's nipple, the fellatio, the nausea, and the vomiting of later years (expulsion of the love object). On the other hand, her feelings of unworthiness and unwillingness to die and the general feeling of depression emanated from the introjected superego, the first love object, or her father. For despite his shortcomings, she loved him; he was a domineering personality, quite able, and very highly regarded outside of his own home and family. She loved him and feared him; throughout her life she struggled with this infantile father; her depressions were also meant to bribe him for her past wrongdoings, thus permitting her to do wrong afterward. Every attack could be traced back to some disappointment of the present which was only a repetition compulsion of something similar in early life.

Thus the last attack appeared while her husband was away on business in California. There was some talk of her accompanying him on the business trip and prolonging it into a few weeks' vacation. After her heart had been set on it, he changed his mind, remarking bluntly that she had had enough holidays already. She was terribly disappointed, but said nothing to him. Her attack was ushered in by a dream in which "she was a child crying and clinging to her father who was about to go away with some woman." The woman in the dream was her mother and the whole picture was a familiar reproduction of her early childhood. She always made a scene when her parents left her at home, and was often spanked for crying continuously until they returned. When she did not cry, she usually did something naughty which merited punishment. She then was justly afraid that her transgressions would be discovered and that she would be punished for them. It was the father, her superego, whom she exchanged for his orderly, for her dentist, and for her husband. It was this fused personality that played the great part in all her attacks. Her ambivalence toward him expressed itself in the depressions and exaltations. In the former she feared his wrath and humbly surrendered to his punishment. She yielded to the tortures of the superego and was willing to die. Having lost her father's love, there was nothing to live for. The life instinct (hunger and love) receded, and the death instinct, in the form of sadism directed to herself, took full possession of her. During the depression, she was not only rejected by her father, but by her suffering she, as it were, bribed him, or bought immunity for the future. When to save herself she merged into a hypomanic state, she was again at peace with her father— she had his love; the death instinct receded, and the life instinct, in the form of excessive eating, drinking, and loving (hunger and love), assumed full sway for the time being.

It would have been impossible in the time at my disposal to have presented all of Freud's contributions to psychiatry from 1892 till 1939. I should like to have been able to say more about the vast region of the unconscious, the existence of which some suspected and even gazed at distantly, but into which no one ventured before Freud. There is much more to be said about Freud's concept of sex on which I have touched only cursorily. Indeed, the best I could do under the circumstances was to skim over some of the problems whose depths I could not penetrate. I have, however, endeavored to show here how Freud actually shaped the instrument by which man can now learn to know himself and to evaluate everything in the true sense of "Know thyself" and "Man is the measure of all things." Freud's contributions thus surpass everything that was brought into psychiatry before him. In making this statement, I am not at all unmindful of all the other scientists who have enriched this field in many directions during the last fifty years, but it was Sigmund Freud who occupied the center of the stage through his daring, original, and fundamental discoveries. Certainly no one before him has contributed so much to the knowledge of man through man himself.

He started with the riddle of hysteria, the prototype of all neuroses, then penetrated into the depth of all the other peculiar mental manifestations, and thus laid bare their meanings and origins. What he demonstrated was that these abnormalities represented nothing but deviations from the paths that were forcibly laid out by civilization. For although some feel that civilization is now a second nature, only a few, if any, can as yet glide smoothly on its tracks. After Freud had grasped the relations of the neuroses to modern life, he concluded that "hysteria is caricature of an artistic creation; compulsion neurosis, a caricature of religion; and paranoia, a caricature of a philosophic system." [8] He thus tells us that the neuroses are asocial phenomena, that they accomplish privately what society has produced in ages through collective effort. But art, religion, and philosophy, of which these neuroses are caricatures, have developed with the dawn of civilization as the greatest outlets of mankind. They represent the crystallizations of man's creative efforts to countervail the hostile forces of

[8] *Totem* and *Taboo,* in *Freud's Basic Writings,* p. 863.

nature. Hence the systems of religion, art, and philosophy by which we now live are basically of the same origin as the neuroses. The neurotics and psychotics who are thus striving to produce new forms of art, new religions, and new philosophies of life clearly show that they are unable to accept the existing modes of expression and that they wish to improve or change them in conformity with their own needs.[9] For the so-called normal or average man, as Bleuler puts it, "is a product of adaptation to conditions and must consequently always hobble along somewhat behind his needs." But as psychiatrists, we know that almost everything new in civilization is initiated and furthered by those who are one-sided in their development. "Psychopaths and insane, such as Mohammed, Luther, Loyola, Rousseau, Pestalozzi, Napoleon and Robert Meyer, have influenced the course of our civilization in a fateful or beneficent manner." [10] A constitutional and personal history of the founders of the new religions in this country, and that of the founders of the modern-art movements, will amply confirm this view. Every psychiatrist occasionally sees world reformers, prophets or fanatical politicians who, if they could put their views in operation, would outdo Hitler in his madness. The line between normal and abnormal is extremely vague; hence no psychiatrist worthy of his name can ignore the basic problems of modern life. That the psychotic urge if not curbed works incalculable harm to the whole civilized world is now well demonstrated. For living as we do—officially, at least, under the aegis of the golden rule—we are prone to forget that these ideals underlying all religions and codes of law of Western civilization were promulgated by Moses and Jesus, idealists who seemingly took no account of the instinctual forces that dominate mankind. The ethical demands that Judaism and Christianity have thus imposed on the average citizen produce a continuous strain which in the field of sexuality may result in neurotic reactions and in other fields in distorted characters and in a constant readiness of the suppressed impulses to enforce their gratifications. As Freud puts it:

[9] Those inclined to speak in terms of biology might call such innovators "single variations" (Darwin) or "mutations," in the sense of De Vries.

[10] Bleuler: *op. cit.*

"Anyone thus forced to react continually to precepts that are not the expressions of his impulses lives, psychologically speaking, beyond his means and may be objectively described as a hypocrite, whether he is clearly conscious of this difference or not." [11] But as experience shows, the tenets of the golden rule can be maintained only by force of arms, which is in itself a product of hatred. Indeed, only when we study the individual by Freud's methods can we understand the blind forces that sway us. I say sway us, because even the sanest among us are not so responsible for their actions as they imagine. *Du glaubst zu schieben, du wirst geschoben* (You believe that you shove but you are shoved), said Goethe.

[11] Freud: *Reflections on War and Death*, p. 28, translated by A. A. Brill and Alfred Kuttner, Moffat, Yard and Co., 1918.

ELEVEN

PSYCHOANALYSIS, ART, AND RELIGION

JUDGING from his works and from my personal knowledge of him, Freud's great interests, besides his studies of the neuroses, were the arts and religion. This was undoubtedly sensed by Max Pollak, the artist who made the well-known etching of Freud. He depicts Freud sitting at his desk in the attitude of writing, or rather reflecting over something that he is about to write down. Facing him on his desk there stand many statuettes which those familiar with his home recall as miniature reproductions of Egyptians. To the left of him there hangs a picture the details of which cannot be seen on the etching but which I recall as that of an Egyptian physician. Freud told me that he had collected all these *objets d'art* during his vacation travels. Whenever I visited him and saw him thus surrounded by Egyptian kings and godheads, I was fascinated but explained it to myself by his interest in art. I will show later that it really represented his great interest in religion.

I also recall that on the right of his desk there hung a plaster bas-relief of a beautifully striding Roman *virgo*, a reproduction of the original in the Vatican Museum. Freud first saw the picture of this young Roman woman on the title page of Wilhelm Jensen's book which he later analyzed.[1] Although he applied his analytic technique to literary works in *The Interpretation of Dreams*, this was his first attempt to apply the technique of dream interpretation to a whole book. In 1910 he ventured still further into the realm of art in his masterful work on Leonardo da Vinci.[2] Indeed, his interest in the arts is seen throughout his works.

His absorbing interest in religion was even deeper. As men-

---

[1] The book appeared in 1903, and Freud's analysis of it, entitled "Der Wahn und die Träume" (Delusion and Dream) in W. Jensen's *Gradiva*, appeared in 1907.

[2] Translated by A. A. Brill, New York, Dodd Mead and Co.

tioned above, he himself felt that his course in life was influenced by the Bible stories which were read to him before he himself could read. In 1907 he wrote a paper on "Zwangshandlungen und Religionsübung" [3] in which he compared the obsessive behavior of compulsive neurotics to religious ceremonials, upon which he later dilated in other works.

In a letter dated January 1, 1912, he wrote: "Meine nächste Arbeiten werden sich mit der Psychologie der Wilden beschäftigen als Einleitung zur Religionspsychologie." (My next works will be devoted to the psychology of savages as an introduction to the psychology of religion.) He subsequently published three separate papers which were later embodied into his work *Totem and Taboo*,[4] wherein he shows the remarkable resemblance between the psychic life of savages and neurotics. Comparing the findings of Darwin, Frazer, Robertson Smith, Atkinson, and others—which go back as far as possible into prehistory—with the results of his analytic discoveries, Freud showed how religion and other moral and social institutions had their origin in the slaying of the primeval father of the horde by his rebellious sons. Leaning on these authors, he showed how this slain father was later replaced by the totem animal which was treated in the same manner as the primeval father. It was taboo to all members of the clan who bore its name and believed they descended from it. They were not only forbidden to hunt or eat it, but in some cases they were not allowed to touch or even look at it.[5]

On the other hand, the members of the clan stressed their relationship to the totem animal by dressing in its skin and by tatooing its image upon their bodies. This identification was carried out in deed and word at births, at initiations into manhood, and at funeral obsequies and, according to W. Robertson Smith, the totem animal was also killed and devoured ceremoniously on solemn occasions. Bearing in mind the resemblances between the

[3] *Sammlung kleiner Schriften*, Zweite Folge, p. 122; English translation by McWatters, *Collected Papers*, vol. II.

[4] Translated by A. A. Brill, in *Freud's Basic Writings*, p. 807.

[5] A survival of totem animals, which still exists in our times, are the wolves kept in the cage at the steps of the Capitol in Rome and the bears in the pit at Bern.

behavior of the horde toward the primeval father and that of the clan toward the totem animal, Freud concludes that the Christian idea of man's "original sin is undoubtedly an offense against God, the father, and if Christ redeems mankind from the weight of original sin by sacrificing his own life, he forces us to the conclusion that this sin was murder. According to the law of retaliation which is deeply rooted in human feeling, a murder can be atoned only by the sacrifice of another life; the self-sacrifice points to a blood-guilt. And if this sacrifice of one's own life brings about a reconciliation with God, the father, then the crime which must be expiated can only have been the murder of the father." [6] There are numerous survivals of this prehistoric drama in legends and fairy tales and in phenomena found in child analysis, but the rite of the Christian communion, wherein the devout symbolically incorporate the blood and flesh of their God, reproduces the inner meaning of the totem feast.

In our civilization the totem animal is represented by animal emblems of empires, kingdoms, and even republics, whose rulers are often treated as totem animals. For the lion, the bear, and the eagle, which were and still are the emblems of most civilized Europe, command respect and fear through their aggression and rapacity. In the Egyptian hieroglyphs, the king was represented by the hawk and the word Habsburg originally was *Habichtsburg* or Hawkshurst. The eagle was the emblem of Czarist Russia, of Austria, and of Germany and, interestingly enough, our forefathers who rebelled against tyranny and founded a democracy nevertheless selected the bald eagle as our national emblem. Benjamin Franklin objected to the bald eagle as a bird of "bad moral character" and expressed his preference for the turkey, "a much more respectable bird and withal a true original native of America." [7]

[6] *Totem and Taboo*, p. 924.

[7] Despite the official selection of the bald eagle, which some said looked like a *dindon*, or turkey, the latter was somehow endowed with the attributes of a totem animal. For it has ever since been our real national bird. It is carefully reared and protected only to be slain and devoured by all good Americans on the most solemn annual celebration of this nation, a day on which the earthly father proclaims thanks to the Father in Heaven. On the

The modern survival of the prehistoric father murder is the Oedipus complex which represents the struggle between the son and his father. The little boy who has not yet learned to love his enemy, as Christianity enjoins, considers everyone who offers any obstacles to the attainment of his wishes as an enemy. Since the father, the ruler of the house, stands between him and his mother, from whom everything good flows, he is perforce his son's greatest rival. Every man has had dreams based on wishes to get rid of the father in order to remain united to the mother. Lest some be shocked at such monstrous thoughts, I wish to remind them that all dreams emanate from repressions and that they occur only in those who cannot entertain such wishes in the waking state. As Plato put it: "The virtuous man contents himself with dreaming of that which the wicked man does in actual life." As civilization cannot openly countenance any hostility of children to parents, "honor thy father and mother" forms one of the great pillars of civilization, the Oedipus complex disappears,[8] and its place is taken by the superego which henceforth harbors all moral restrictions and ideal perfections imposed upon the son by his father. The superego is thus not just a precipitate of the parents but of the parents' parents as well as their substitutes. It is, in fine, the bearer of the traditions and cultural assets of the past generations. To put it in the words of Freud: "Mankind never lives completely in the present; the ideologies of the superego perpetuate the past, the traditions of the race and the people which yield but slowly to the influence of the present and to new developments, and, so long as they work through the superego, play an important part in man's life quite independently of economic conditions." [9]

---

other hand, the American eagle has been viciously persecuted, almost to extinction. It thus seems that the *ambivalence* of love and hate ordinarily meted out to the totem animal in primitive society still exists among us in disguised, albeit practical, form. Instead of one totem animal, the bald eagle, an inedible bird of prey, we have two, one just to kill and the other to kill and devour ceremoniously—a sensible American solution to the father ambivalence.

[8] Freud: "Der Untergang des Oedipuskomplexes," *Internat. Ztschr. f. Psychoanal.*, vol. X, 1924.

[9] *New Introductory Lectures*, p. 96, translated by Sprott, New York, W. W. Norton and Co.

Thus through the study of dreams Freud gained an insight not only into the individual's but also into the race's past. For the same technique of interpretation made it possible to find the meaning of fairy tales, folklore, and myths and to demonstrate the resemblance between the psychic life of savages and that of neurotics. But as neurotics represent no special species of mankind and as their only distinctive characteristic is a greater sensitiveness to stimuli, we can understand why they resemble primitives of today and probably those of yesterday. This also explains why the neurotic reactions are often baffling, especially when we attempt to correlate them with the patient's past. Discussing the situation, Freud states: "When we study the reactions to early traumas, we are often enough surprised to find that they do not strictly adhere to what the individual himself has experienced, but deviate from it in a manner to fit far better into some model of a phylogenetic event, and in general can only be explained through that influence." [10] This is quite evident in tracing the reactions to the Oedipus and castration complexes, in studying animal phobias, and especially the phobia of being eaten by the father. Such studies point to a direct transition from the unconscious present to the past and, in a way, bridge the behavior reactions of present-day man with those of prehistory.

In 1914 there appeared a very interesting paper on "Michelangelo's Moses." [11] It was written by Freud but, for reasons that will be discussed later, he withheld his name from it. Here Freud not only delved deeply into art but also into religion. The whole discussion revolved around the question—what Michelangelo wished to represent by his depiction of Moses. In his introduction to the paper, Freud stated that works of art, especially literature and sculpture, had always exerted a powerful influence on him, and that he had often spent much time before them endeavoring to understand them in his own way. He wished to discover the meaning of their effect on him. Being rationalistic, or perhaps of an analytic turn of mind, he rebelled against being moved by

[10] Freud: *Der Mann Moses und die monotheistische Religion*, p. 177, Amsterdam, Albert de Lange, 1939.
[11] "Moses des Michelangelo," *Imago*, 1914.

something without knowing why; and as he could not discover the meaning of music, he was almost incapable of obtaining any pleasure from it.

Anyone reading this paper will observe, besides the artistic elements contained therein, Freud's even greater interest in the personality of Moses himself. After reviewing the numerous assumptions on the meaning of Michelangelo's masterpiece, he accepted Thodes' view that the artist "created an image of a passionate leader of mankind who, conscious of his divine mission as lawgiver, meets the uncomprehending opposition of men." [12] If we bear in mind that the figure of Moses was impressed upon Freud while he was still a child listening to the Bible stories, we can venture the assumption that unconsciously, perhaps consciously, he identified himself with this great leader of his people. For he, too, was a passionate leader of mankind, conscious of his mission as a teacher, as an expositor of the dark recesses of the mind; he, too, was confronted by the blind opposition of men. It was perhaps this identification that prevented him, who had always preached frankness, from affixing his name to a work which on the surface showed nothing that warranted concealment. It would also explain why he surrounded himself with statuettes of Egyptian kings and deities, and why his last work was again dedicated to Moses and his religion. Perhaps he felt that someone might detect him in the figure of Moses. There is no doubt that the great lawgiver fascinated him, for years later he saw fit to write a supplement to this paper in which he no longer concealed his authorship.[13]

But let us return to Freud's interest in religion. In 1927 he wrote *Die Zukunft einer Illusion* (Future of an Illusion) [14] in which he goes into the deeper relations between religion and culture and the relation of religion to mankind. Both here and elsewhere he frankly states that he was not religious and that he was "as little

[12] *Imago*, III, 23, 1914; English translation by Alix Strachey in *Collected Papers*, vol. IV.
[13] "Nachtrag über den Moses des Michelangelo," *Gesam. Schriften*, XI, 409.
[14] Internat. Psychoanalyt. Verlag; English translation by Robson-Scott, New York, Horace Liveright, 1928.

an adherent of the Jewish religion as of any other religion." [15]
He stated that he considered all religions as most important objects
of scientific interest, but that he did not share the emotional feeling
associated with them. Freud has been roundly criticized for his
views on religion, despite the fact that he did not express anything that many scientists have not said before.

In his book *Das Unbehagen in der Kultur* (Civilization and Its
Discomforts),[16] he again devotes considerable space to the religion
of the average man. He states that the latter does not bother about
the sources of his religious feeling but has in mind a system of
precepts and promises that on the one hand explains to him the
riddles of this world with enviable perfection and on the other
hand gives him the assurance that a heedful providence watches
over his life and that present-day deprivations will be made good
in the hereafter. Such a providence can be conceived by the average man only as a wonderful father who alone is capable of knowing the needs of mankind and who grants its prayers if approached
with proper humility. Such a concept, according to Freud, is
altogether foreign to reality, but he is reminded of Goethe's saying: "He who possesses science and arts has also religion. He who
does not possess these two should have religion." (*Wer Wissen-
schaft und Kunst besitzt, hat auch Religion; Wer jene beiden nicht
besitzt, der habe Religion.*) Here Goethe contrasts science and
art, the greatest accomplishments of culture with religion, and
does not seem to believe that the average man can get along without religion. This seems to concur with Freud's views as given
previously.

Considering the amount of space Freud devoted to religion in
the works enumerated, in *The Interpretation of Dreams*, and in
his autobiography, it is quite obvious that religion had a fascinating
interest for him. He was not, as we have shown above, religious
in the ordinary sense of the term but, like his kinsman Spinoza,
who turned away from Jewish orthodoxy and nevertheless became the "God-intoxicated man," as Novalis called him, Freud too

---

[15] Letter to the editor of the *Jüdische Presszentrale*, Zurich, February 26,
1925.
[16] Internat. Psychoanalyt. Verlag, Wien, 1930.

could not desist from occupying himself with religion. In a letter dated December 4, 1911, he wrote: *"Ich bin von meiner Studien über Religionspsychologie ausserordentlich in Angriff genommen."* (I am extraordinarily absorbed in the study of the psychology of religion.)

This great interest was surely not due entirely to the fact that he was a Jew who suffered the effects of anti-Semitism almost from early boyhood until his death. Almost every Jew goes through similar experiences, especially those who attain some prominence in life. From my numerous discussions with him of the Jewish problem in so far as it affected him and his children, he was always quite objective about it. Long before the first World War, he expressed to me his deep concern about his children's future in Austria, and that was at a time when Austria was still a great nation and seemed to offer many opportunities for young people. When I expressed these last views to him, he said prophetically that everything might look nice on the surface, but the storm might come at any time. Yet he was deeply attached to Vienna and when I and others urged him to leave Austria when the political situation was growing increasingly menacing, he said: "I shall leave Vienna only if the Nazis come here." And that is exactly what he did.

One might ask why Freud who was not emotionally religious should have given so much thought to it in his studies of the neuroses. In his introductory remarks to the first edition of *The Interpretation of Dreams*, Freud stated that in turning his interest to dreams, he had not overstepped the bounds of psychopathology. For the dream proved to be the first link in a chain of abnormal psychic structures comprising also hysterical symptoms, obsessions, and delusions. But although the dream is not so important practically as the other psychic structures, its theoretical value as a paradigm is even greater; for "he who cannot explain the origin of dream images will strive in vain to understand phobias, obsessions, and delusions as well as their therapeutic importance."

In his effort to elucidate the methods of dream interpretation, Freud had to choose between material from his own dreams or from those of his patients. He decided against the use of the latter material because he thought that dreams of neurotics would unduly complicate his demonstrations. On the other hand, in using his own dreams, he was forced to expose more of his intimate psychic life than he liked. He frankly admitted that he disguised some of his indiscretions by omissions and substitutions, and that this detracted materially from the value of the examples he used. But he begged the reader to consider his difficult position and show forbearance, and asked those who might be offended by any of the reported dreams to concede freedom of thought at least to dream life.

Despite this explanation, Freud suffered much for his candor and he did not recommend it to others. Anyone experienced in analysis knows that free associations to dreams bring up some of the dreamer's most intimate thoughts and feelings. And as Freud illustrated the mechanisms of dream interpretation, he naturally had to record frankly what one ordinarily keeps to himself. Many of these candidly expressed thoughts dealt with religion and anti-Semitism, and if Freud had been an obscure nobody, no notice would have been taken of what he said, but since he had aroused the world by his new and revolutionary thoughts, his views on religion offered a fertile ground for attack. Here I am reminded of a physician who had always been in the good graces of his church and quite active in its charities. Discussing the Immaculate Conception, he once said to his wife that as a physician this was the only tenet of his religion that he never could fully assimilate. Twenty-four years later when they had quarreled and separated, his wife told an official of the church that her husband was an infidel who did not believe in the Immaculate Conception. As a result he was not only relieved of all his activities, but was practically driven out of the church. He assured me that to his knowledge he had never expressed this view to anyone else, although he admitted that he could not accept this doctrine in the literal sense.

Freud committed two sins: first, he admitted that he was not religious and, second, he showed that he was more or less vulnerable to religious persecution. Many of Freud's opponents, some of them pronounced psychopaths, took advantage of his frankness and then tried to expose him to the world as an irreligious Jew obsessed by sex. Many papers and at least one book were written on what Freud left out in the analysis of his dreams. Each of these critics or mind readers had a particular ax to grind, yet all of them directed their attacks against Freud's religion. The anti-Semites accused him of trying to foist Judaism and sex on the world, while his Jewish critics reproached him for not being a good Jew.

Since I went through similar experiences here soon after I became Freud's translator and expositor, I can say that most of those who attacked him on the grounds of sex could be classified into two categories: those who suffered from marked sexual repressions that they could barely control and who were consequently irritated by anything that savored even lightly of sex, and those who felt consciously guilty of violating the conventional sex morality; the latter often react to anything said about sex as if they themselves were exposed. Thus I had heard for years of a woman who went out of her way to preach against psychoanalysis because it was "too sexual." She had come to me for analysis and I found her unfit for this kind of treatment. She was morally oligophrenic; she could not tell the truth. I knew from three different sources that she was leading a very bad sexual life, yet after four interviews, during which I questioned her about it, she stoutly denied everything but tried foolishly to question me about one of my patients to whom she had made bold advances. Her gratuitous repetitions that psychoanalysis was "too sexual" was a clumsy form of self-defense. By objecting to psychoanalysis on the ground of sex, people would think that she was sexually above reproach. Consulting me was an effort to get help after she had gone through very disagreeable experiences, but her weak character kept her from telling me the facts; she could not face reality.

However, the majority of sex objectors react to unconscious strivings. By hurling invectives at Freud and psychoanalysis, they in a way disburden their own repressed sexuality. For there was nothing in Freud's family life that could in any way be construed as improper. Nor is there anything in his work on sex that can possibly be interpreted as offensive or even suggestive. The worst that I heard from those who seriously read his work on sex was that they did not always understand it. On the other hand, serious students of medicine and biology entertained a very high opinion of Freud's work on sex.

Soon after my English translations of Freud's works appeared here, I received letters from so-called Jewish scientists accusing Freud of crypto-anti-Semitism. One of them was angry because Freud used many Jewish jokes to illustrate some of his theories on wit and humor. One orthodox Jewish psychoanalyst accused Freud of flirting with the idea of accepting Catholicism in order to realize his thwarted ambitions. Another Jewish medical biographer informed me that he had written a biography of Freud but tore it up after he had read Freud's book *Moses and Monotheism*.[17]

That his antagonists and self-appointed analysts should have taken his religion as the *point d'appui* for their speculations and attacks is quite understandable. Religion has often been used as an excuse for persecution and brutality, and not only against Jews. Moreover, experience teaches that emotions are suggestible, nay contagious.[18] He who is under the spell of some complex is likely to transmit its affectivity to others. It is an unfortunate fact that almost every Jew is distressed and discomfited because of his religion, though he rarely speaks of it. But as we said previously, Freud had to air many situations in which his career was impeded because he was a Jew, and throughout his analytic life he manifested an extraordinary interest in religion amounting almost to a complex. I use the word "almost" advisedly because there was nothing about any of these episodes that was really unconscious or fully repressed. Yet it was this *Complex-bereitschaft* (complex-readiness), as Bleuler called it, which impressed his antagonists as Freud's Achilles' heel. They were surprised to hear him speak so frankly about the disabilities from which he suffered as a Jew, not understanding that he could express himself so freely only because he was never deeply impressed by religion. In the letter in which he speaks of his attitude to religion, he also said: "My youth was spent in a period when our free-minded teachers of religion

---

[17] Translated by Katherine Jones, New York, Alfred A. Knopf, 1939.
[18] Bleuler: *Affectivity, Suggestibility, Paranoia*, translated by Ricksher, New York State Hospital Press, 1912.

placed no value on their pupils' acquisition of knowledge in the Hebrew language and literature." From my knowledge of the Jews of the former Austro-Hungarian Empire, I can state that any Jewish boy whose Hebrew education was neglected was not brought up religiously. Freud's father, an intelligent liberal, evidently did not impose any dogmatic religion on his children. Mrs. Anna Freud Bernays, Freud's sister who has been living in New York City since 1892, told me the same thing personally, and in her very interesting paper on the early life of the Freud family, she mentions nothing of religion.[19]

Not having been brought up by the dictum, "The fear of the Lord is the beginning of knowledge," which every God-fearing father usually implants in his son, Freud never developed a religious background. His father, judging from all accounts, was a benign and understanding counselor rather than the severe disciplinarian who serves as a model for a strong superego. Freud's freedom of thought and his courage in the face of dangerous persecution were, in my opinion, largely if not entirely due to this factor. His seeming "religion-complex" was, therefore, not determined by unconscious repressed impressions but by disagreeable experiences which he clearly remembered. The first time he was affected by anti-Semitism occurred indirectly at the age of ten or twelve when his father related to him the insulting episode that occurred before Freud was born.[20] Judging by the associations Freud gives to it, we can assume that he was deeply touched by it. But we must not forget that this happened during his pubescent period and that although it produced a disagreeable impression, it was not repressed in the psychoanalytic sense of the term. The first time he was directly affected by religious discrimination was when he enrolled in the university. Henceforth he had to cope with the problem in the same manner as every other Jew, and as he always had his feet firmly on the ground, he adjusted himself to the situation through self-analysis and sublimation. At no time did he attempt to hide his Judaism, and although he was not emotionally

---

[19] "My Brother Sigmund Freud," *The American Mercury*, November, 1940.
[20] *The Interpretation of Dreams*, in *Freud's Basic Writings*, p. 260.

religious, he always felt a strong feeling of kinship with his race and nurtured the same in his children.[21]

The analyst, mentioned previously, who tried to show from Freud's dreams that Freud thought (unconsciously) of changing his religion in order to improve his lot, expressed a commonplace idea which many a Jew has not only considered consciously but actually has put into operation. But as is well known, conversions occur only under special emotional states which never existed in Freud. Some like Heinrich Heine—a most sensitive poet—accepted baptism as a salvation for his Jewish disabilities, but Freud, to whom religion was nothing but a remnant of one's childhood dependence, could never have resorted to such evasions of reality. He followed another Jew, Spinoza, who solved his religious conflicts by his formula: *Humanas actiones non ridere, nec lugere, nec detestare sed intelligere.* (Human actions should not be mocked, not lamented, nor execrated but should be understood.) Spinoza was once asked by his Christian landlady whether he thought she could be saved by her religion. "Your religion," he answered, "is good; you need not look for any other in order to be saved, provided you lead a peaceful and pious life." [22] Freud would have given the same advice to any devout believer. Notwithstanding his conclusion that religion was an illusion, he readily admitted that it had performed a great service for mankind in so far as it had contributed toward restraining asocial instincts. He was not fanatically opposed to religion, but as he tried hard to evaluate all the mainsprings of human behavior, he perforce thought also of religion and strove to explain it. In his own words: "I have said nothing that other and better men have not said before me in a much more complete, forcible and impressive way. . . . I have merely—that is the only thing that is new in my statement—added a certain psychological foundation to the critique of my predecessors." [23]

The formulation of this psychological foundation began in his paper *Obsessive Acts and Religious Practices* (see p. 186). It may

[21] See Freud's letter on page 47 of this book.
[22] *Spinoza Gespräche*, p. 117, Gebhard, Leipzig, 1914.
[23] Freud: *The Future of an Illusion*, p. 62, translated by Robson-Scott.

be assumed that this paper contains the germ plasm of an idea that had been hitherto more or less inactive but that gradually gained momentum as he elaborated his system of thought. For it is in this work that he calls attention to the close connection between the neurosis and religion, in which he demonstrates for the first time the remarkable resemblance between the psychic mechanisms of obsessions and those of religious ceremonials, both in their origin and development. Thus, solemn acts of religious rites, like obsessive ceremonials, must be performed with absolute precision. If for some reason the smallest item is omitted or in any way varied, both the neurotic and the devout believer suffer pangs of conscience. Moreover, the execution of both obsessive acts and of religious ceremonials is sharply separated from all other activities—there must be no disturbance during such functions. All believers, regardless of the religion they profess, center all their feelings on their prayers and ceremonials which they perform in a stereotyped manner and in complete isolation whenever possible. Lecky [24] relates that Saint Boniface struck dead a man who went about with an ape and cymbal because he had unintentionally disturbed him at his prayers. The same strong desire not to be disturbed is also manifested by compulsive neurotics when they go through their ceremonials. Thus, the "dog-god" neurotic (see p. 33) had to repeat the ticlike upward motions with his arms five times consecutively if he happened to be disturbed in his performance, or if he was not absolutely sure that the upswing of his arms was exerted with sufficient force. In order to perform the obsessive motions properly, he locked himself in the washroom whenever possible. The compulsive neurotic F., who cured himself of constipation by throwing a pin into the heart region of a girl image, went through a most complicated ceremonial in the execution of it which took over two regular-sized pad pages to describe. If something interfered with the meticulous performance of the ceremonial, the desired result was not achieved and the whole process had to be repeated. On the other hand, as time went on he, like many other compulsive neurotics, was able to hasten the performance through some short cuts, but these, too, had to

[24] *History of European Morals*, II, 122.

be done accurately and thoroughly. The following case will illustrate a typical compulsive neurotic behavior and its meaning.

A young woman of twenty-six could not bear the idea of wearing jewelry, but since she was afraid to admit this, she had to wear some on occasion. Before putting on any ornament she went through the following ceremonial: She waited until about five minutes before she had to leave her home, then bowed her head in an attitude of prayer, counted up to one hundred in sums of twenty-five as quickly as she could, then ran to her jewelry box, opened and closed it four times, grasped the ring or lavallière and threw it on the floor so that it rolled away from her. She then began to look for it with great excitement; sometimes she could not find it and had to go to the party without it. This was always accompanied by a feeling of marked relief; usually, however, she found it, and as she put it on, she had to count again in sums of twenty-five until she reached her destination.

Analysis showed the following: Her mother had a diamond sunburst which the girl had craved years before when she was about to attend a very important dance. She asked her mother to let her wear it and the latter replied: "My daughter, in one hundred years when I am dead you will have it—not before, unless your own husband gets you one." Sometime later, she was to go to another dance where she was particularly anxious to make a good impression, and while dressing, the thought suddenly flashed through her mind: "If your mother were dead, you would have the sunburst." This thought frightened her because she recognized it as a wish that her mother should die. She strove hard to banish it from her mind, and to punish herself for entertaining such a horrible thought she decided not to go to the party, but soon changed her mind and went nevertheless. The reproaches continually disturbed her throughout the dance and during the next day, until she vowed not to wear any jewelry on her neck for a whole year. This ban was soon generalized not to wear any jewelry, a vow she found difficult to adhere to because her mother and others in her home often suggested and even urged that she wear some ornament. As time went on, she gradually developed the ceremonials previously described and completely forgot the episode that gave origin to them. Her obsessive acts were entirely unconscious to her. Further investigation showed that counting to one hundred signified that her mother was now dead; counting in series of twenty-fives, which was her age, was meant to advance her own age to one hundred. This signified both the wish that her mother be dead and the self-punishment that she, too, be dead for entertaining this hostile feeling against her mother. Opening and closing the box four times in succession had the same meaning, and sometimes served as a short cut for the whole obsessive act. Throwing the ornament on the floor expressed the endopsychic conflict. It signified a sort of compromise between coveting and rejecting her mother's jewels. Hence the feeling of relief when the ring sometimes rolled under the furniture and could not be recovered for the time being. Her hurrying throughout the procedure represented an identification with her mother who was never on time when she was to go out with her father to some social function. He often had to call out, "Hurry, it is late!" This also signified that she herself was now married and was hurrying to go out with her own husband—a fulfillment of the condition originally set by her mother, "unless your husband will buy you one." Holding her head in an attitude of prayer while she went through the compulsive acts meant to ask forgiveness for the death wish against her mother.

This is only a very brief outline of an obsessive ceremonial and is told in order to show its resemblance to a religious rite. When the patient sometimes became confused during the obsessive routine, she had to repeat everything over and over again, and the emotional tension thus engendered was sometimes so intense that she had to remain at home.

However, the differences between obsessive acts and religious rites are just as glaring. Thus obsessive ceremonials differ in each neurotic, while religious observances are usually the same in any particular religion. The compulsive neurotic realizes that his acts are silly and hence conceals his obsessions as much as he can; the devout believer, on the other hand, manifests no such feelings, and goes through his religious rites at the set time wherever he happens to find himself. In this respect the compulsion neurosis represents now a semicomic, now a semitragic caricature of a private religion.

This sharp distinction between neurotic and religious ceremonials vanishes, however, as soon as obsessions are subjected to analysis. We then find that though individually determined, they are as full of meaning as religious ceremonials. To be sure, the example previously described showed that the meaning of the compulsive act was unconscious to the patient, but the same is also true of the ceremonials observed by the average pious observer. He, too, goes through the rites without really understanding their meaning. The ordinary Catholic does not know the meaning of the Latin used by the priest, any more than the average Jew understands the Hebrew he mumbles in praying. As a matter of fact, most of the religious ceremonials are symbolic expressions, the meanings of which are known only to few of its learned votaries.

However, the compulsive neurotic demonstrates by his obsessions, doubts, and phobias that he is dominated by an *unconscious feeling* of guilt of which he is ignorant. This guilt came into being as a result of early psychic experiences and is constantly refreshed by new temptations of recent origin. As was shown previously (see p. 199), at the beginning of the formation of the obsession the patients were more or less conscious of its meaning. They knew, in a general way, that they had to do this or omit that in order to avert some evil, but they did not know the connection between the manifested anxiety and the content of the threat. In fine, the ceremonial begins as a defense measure against some disaster which in time becomes so complicated through obsessive associations and generalizations that the patient entirely forgets the original situation.

One of my patients, a man of about forty, suffered from the compulsion that "Mr. G. stole $40,000." This idea had been obsessing him for many years with fluctuating intensity. Besides knowing such a person rather vaguely, the patient knew that the rest was pure fantasy. Analysis showed the following.

Mrs. G.'s daughter Sally had been in primary school with the patient at the age of eight or nine. She sat across the aisle from him, and because he had some obscene thought about her, he was afraid that he would be punished by her father.

The idea that G. stole $40,000 gave the following associations: "I cannot say whether I think it or say it, but if I should say it, Sally might hear it and tell her father. Her father would then sue my father, who would spank the stuffings out of me for getting him into trouble. In fact, he might even kill me." These ideas forcibly obtruded themselves on his mind despite the fact that he had not seen Sally for at least twenty years.

As he grew older, the obsessive phobia became extensively generalized. The fear of uttering this thought then spread to the phobia that he might write it, and he then avoided all books and papers. He even feared that he might scratch the thought with his fingernails. He could not, however, stop thinking of the number 4. He counted it in his mind, touched things four times and contemplated the multiples of 4. In time, he found himself stepping over cracks in the sidewalk in a series of 4. All these phobias and obsessions resulted in a monophobia, "I feared that if I were alone, I might do those things." Further analysis showed that number 4 was always an obsessive number to the patient. He first imagined that he liked the number 4 because it differed from number 13, an unlucky number. Number 13 is a primary number; number 4 is the smallest number that is not prime. Hence, number 4 must be a lucky number. As he grew older, he had the compulsion to analyze any number that he happened to come across for multiples of 4. For example: "Number $28 = 7 \times 4$, and it therefore has a good quality. Number $36 = 9 \times 4$, but $9 + 4 = 13$; hence it is not so good." Such examples were multiplied and added continuously. Another elaboration of the 4 was that in reading a line with five words, he had to go back and read the last three words twice, so that the line would be read with eight words, a multiple of 4. The generalizations and ramifications of this phobia, besides the examples given here, are too numerous to mention; they really extended as far as the patient's memory could go.

We can only speak briefly about the origin of this obsessive phobia: like all similar obsessions, it went back to the pregenital period of the patient's life. He was a spoiled child and had great difficulties in giving up his infantile sexual activities. When he was unable or unwilling to empty his bowels, his mother resorted to the following ceremonial: She counted "1, 2, 3, 4" and cried out, "Push hard." It was understood that if successful, he would be rewarded; otherwise, he would be punished. At that period of his existence feces was the most valuable object, of which everybody wished to deprive him. There were other very complex associations, which pointed to identifications of Sally with his first love object—feces—and mother, and of Mr. G. with his own father. The interpretation of the obsession read: "Father robs or robbed me of my love object." [25]

As can be seen, the obsessive formula "Mr. G. stole $40,000" represented an Oedipus conflict which started in the patient's early life, and although in the form presented by the patient at the age of forty it showed nothing of its original configuration, it could, nevertheless, be reconstructed as a protective measure against an unconscious guilt. When the pious believers recite the *Damnatus Sumus*, they feel from the bottom of their hearts that they are miserable sinners and their ceremonials—singing, chanting, swaying or kneeling—are nothing but protective measures against the fear of punishment.

It may be asked why the compulsive neurotic is able to juggle with his superstitions so artfully, often against his better judgment. Freud answers this by stating that the compulsive neurotic is dominated by what he calls the "omnipotence of thought." This phrase was coined by one of Freud's compulsive neurotic patients [26] to designate all those peculiar and uncanny occurrences that seemed to pursue him just as they pursue other obsessive neurotics. "Thus if he happened to think of a person, he was actually confronted with this person as if he had conjured him up; if he inquired suddenly about the state of health of an acquaintance whom he had long missed, he was sure to hear that this acquaint-

---

[25] Cf. Brill, "Determinism in Psychiatry and Psychoanalysis," *Am. J. Psychiat.*, November, 1938.

[26] "Remarks upon a Case of Compulsion Neurosis," *Jahrb. f. Psychoanalyt. u. Psychopathol. Forschungen*, vol. I, 1909.

ance had just died, so that he could believe that the deceased had drawn his attention to himself by telepathic means; if he uttered a half-meant imprecation against a stranger, he could expect to have him die soon thereafter and burden him with the responsibility for his death." [27] But analysis of compulsion neurotics can always explain how such illusions originate and show that the patient himself had contributed toward furthering his superstitious expectations.

The existence of omnipotence of thought is most clearly seen in compulsion neurosis where this primitive mode of thought is frequently expressed in consciousness; but it is also characteristic of childhood and of savages and of other neuroses. "Neurotics," says Freud, "live in a special world in which, as I have elsewhere expressed it, only the 'neurotic standard of currency' counts, that is to say, only things intensively thought of or affectively conceived are effective with them, regardless of whether these things are in harmony with outer reality. The hysteric repeats in his attacks and fixates through his symptoms occurrences which have taken place only in his fantasy, though in the last analysis they go back to real events or have been built up from them. The neurotic's guilty conscience is just as incomprehensible if traced to real misdeeds. . . . The primary obsessive actions of these neurotics are really altogether of a magical nature. If not magic, they are at least anti-magic and are destined to ward off the expectation of evil with which the neurosis is wont to begin." [28]

There is no doubt that religious ceremonials strive to accomplish similar purposes. But whereas the pious observer uses his religious rites to avert evils of the present, e.g. praying for peace, the compulsive neurotic is basically occupied with the past and unconsciously with sexual problems. For even if the obsessive acts began as defense measures against evil wishes that were in no way connected with sex, they invariably develop into substitutes for prohibited sexual acts. With the advance of civilization, the primary instinct of self-preservation gradually became increasingly attenuated. No one in modern society is subjected to the struggle

[27] *Totem and Taboo*, in *Freud's Basic Writings*, p. 873.
[28] *Ibid.*, p. 874.

for existence in the primitive, natural sense of that term. On the contrary, during ordinary times, society assumes the care of the weak and dependent, and the average citizen rarely, if ever, starves or freezes in the manner of his animal forebears. On the other hand, the instinct for the preservation of the species, sex, has not only continued in its primitive form but has become increasingly enhanced with the elimination of hunger and seasonal hardships. Organized society could not, however, exist on "sex freedom" as some benighted preachers of this cult still imagine; hence one of its tasks has always been to regulate and control sex. In historical times, Judaism was the first religion to lay down rigid rules for sexual control, and Christianity, following in its wake, went even further in the enforcement of sexual morality. Since most of the early Christians were direct descendants of nations that had hitherto extolled the sexual instinct, the church fathers had to exert extreme pressure to abrogate sex. Instead of beauty, which was worshiped by the ancient Greeks and Romans, early Christianity in repressing it put a price on ugliness. Since not everyone was constitutionally able to accept the new dicta, modern man became more or less obsessed by the problem of sex and its mode of control. This situation has continued ever since and no matter how a mental conflict starts, it sooner or later becomes tinged with sex and is very often entirely changed by it. Hence when Breuer and Freud began to study hysteria by penetrating into the intimate life of their patients, they found to their surprise that sex played a predominant role in the disease, and as Freud continued these investigations in the other neuroses, he soon promulgated the dictum: "In a normal *vita sexualis* no neurosis is possible."

TWELVE

RELIGION AND TRAUMATIC NEUROSIS

ONE year later, in 1907, Freud demonstrated the close analogy of the mechanisms of the neurosis to those of religion, the concept which gradually matured in his later works, attaining full development in his last book *Moses and Monotheism*. For religion, the strands of which run through the whole fabric of Freud's works, has been a universal expression of mankind from the dawn of civilization. The most primitive tribes everywhere have always been controlled and guided by rules and regulations akin to religion. In his practice, Freud found that many of his patients were positively or negatively influenced by it, and in many, it was directly connected with the neurosis. For whether a patient is a religious paranoiac or a compulsive neurotic, the forces that dominate him are always the same. They represent a struggle between the superego and the id in which the ego, the representative of our cultural, albeit unnatural, life, strives to reconcile our innate love and hatred with the prohibitions and inhibitions of our cultural existence. It is this universal and everlasting struggle in the individual and in the race that Freud demonstrates in his last work and thus forms a direct transition between ontogeny and phylogeny.

The thesis he presents in *Moses and Monotheism* is that the evolution of the psychological structure of monotheism had proceeded along paths that are very similar to the scheme of a neurosis in the individual, particularly of a *traumatic neurosis*. To demonstrate this, Freud delved deeply into the origin of monotheism which is the nucleus of the predominant religions of civilized mankind. Since the Bible is not only an inexhaustible source of information on the origin of religion but also, and particularly, on the personality of Moses, Freud naturally centered his investigation on the Pentateuch. For it is in these books that one can clearly see how conflicts arise as soon as a race is subjected to rules and regulations. One can also observe the effects of yielding to temptations, the ensuing sin, guilt, and retribution, phenomena which, as shown previously, form also the bases of neuroses.

Speaking of traumatic neurosis, Freud wrote: "The state of mind which follows severe mechanical commotions, such as train collisions and other accidents connected with danger to life, has long been described under the name of traumatic neurosis." [1] The pictures such neuroses present are usually the same as those of other neuroses except that they are attributed to some physical injury, frequently to an accidental head injury. The connection between traumas and neuroses is not new in psychoanalysis. Breuer and Freud always stressed this relationship. In their words: "The experience, which generated the original affect, the excitement of which was later converted into a somatic phenomenon, we designate as a *psychic trauma*, and the morbid manifestations which so originated as *hysterical symptoms of traumatic origin*." [2] The traumatic factor was particularly stressed by Freud who in this regard differed with Breuer. The latter, following Charcot, stated that any experience, no matter how trifling, can acquire the importance of a trauma if the patient happens to be in a particular state of mind—in the so-called hypnoid state. As we have seen, Freud rejected this theory by stating that "very often there is not the slightest support for such assumption." [3]

In a symposium on the war neuroses [4] Freud stated that in contrast to the banal neuroses of peacetime, the war neuroses are to be conceived as traumatic neuroses, which are produced or favored by an ego conflict or a disturbance of ego libido. [5] The basic mechanism of the war neuroses is a conflict "between the old peaceful and the new warlike ego, and becomes acute as soon as the old ego is suddenly faced by the danger to his life, forced upon him by the darings of his newly formed parasitic double."

[1] *Jenseits des Lustprinzips*, p. 10, Internat. Psychoanalyt. Verlag, 1920; English translation, *Beyond the Pleasure Principle*, by Hubback.

[2] *Studies in Hysteria, op. cit.*, p. 153.

[3] *Neurosenlehre*, 1st Series, p. 153.

[4] *Zur Psychoanalyse der Kriegsneurosen*, Internat. Psychoanalyt. Verlag, 1919.

[5] This view was confirmed by Abraham, Jones and others.

A civilian army would thus furnish a favorable soil for the development of war neuroses which would be comparatively rare in an army made up of professional soldiers. For the latter are, as a rule, soldiers by choice, or if conscripted they readily adapt themselves to army life. They take their training seriously and therefore soon become hardened for aggressive soldiering. Good examples of this type are the old noncommissioned officers of our army who are so thoroughly identified with their vocation that the hazards of war do not seem to disturb them. It is they who gave rise to the legend, "Old soldiers never die."

I have rarely seen war neuroses in such soldiers, and the few that came to my attention presented an entirely different picture from the general run of such cases. Thus during the first World War I saw a sergeant who was returned from the front for the following reasons: When he joined the army about ten years before the war, his parents were dead and he had two younger brothers and one sister. When the war broke out he had been married six years and had two children. His sister was married, one of his brothers was in the army and the other in the navy. Within a few months after he came to France, he heard successively that his sister had died, that his brother was lost at sea, that his other brother was killed in action, that one of his children had died, and somewhat later that his wife had died and that his other child had fallen out of a fourth-story window and was killed. He was thus bereft of all those dear to him and it seemed that he had nothing to live for. His captain, hearing of his misfortunes and noticing that he was depressed, had him hospitalized and he was then sent home. When I saw him, with Dr. George H. Kirby, he showed a depression which was not, however, of a pathologic nature. He admitted that he was nervous but protested against hospitalization and repeated that since the army was the only thing left to him, he should be allowed to return to combat duty. Since neither Kirby nor I could find any definite neurosis, we concluded that his depression was due to normal grief and recommended that he be restored to active service.

Most war neuroses if accessible to study invariably show the obverse of this picture as will be demonstrated in the following case: [6] In May, 1917, one month after we entered the first World War, an English army officer—case of "shell shock"—came to me for treatment directly from the battle front. After one of the big "drives," the patient was found in an unconscious state under the debris of a building that had been demolished by an explosion. With the exception of a superficial scar on the back of his neck, no organic injuries were found. Yet for about two weeks he was in a semiconscious mental state; when this disappeared, he showed marked tremors, especially of the fingers, and general anxiety. After about two months' hospitalization in France and in England, a military medical commission recommended that he take a vacation far from the scene of war, in Canada or in the United States. A member of the commission, a Dr. Russell, suggested that in the event he chose the States he should consult me in New York. I was quite flattered when the patient told me this, for I was still at an age when one is pleased by recognition from an unknown colleague.

The patient had been brought up in Australia; he was forty-three years old and married. He had been in the British army for many years before the war and as far as he knew had never been neurotically ill. His main symptoms were marked sensitivity to sounds, tremors, and anxiety, which was still in a free-floating state, although some of it expressed itself in phobias and in psychosomatic feelings. He was very timid about meeting people and for the first two months spent most of his time in his room, leaving it only for meals and for visits to me. As he had only four months' leave and hence could not be subjected to a regular psychoanalysis, I resorted to other psychotherapeutic measures to help him to get back to the front. After about two months' treatment, he showed considerable improvement and, encouraged by me, he put on his uniform and began to move about the city. One evening I asked him to dine with me and after a few drinks he spoke more freely than he ever had in my office. In the midst of his talk, he suddenly opened the back of his wrist watch, took a piece of paper out of it

[6] The case was reported in the Bulletin of the New York Academy of Medicine for October, 1942, by Dr. George A. Blakeslee in his presidential address to the New York Neurological Society.

and showing it to me said, "I carried this with me for years." I was amazed when I read "Dr. A. A. Brill, 55 Central Park West," which was where I once lived. He then explained that a medical friend of his in Australia, who had corresponded with me, often spoke to him about my work, and one day after he had read one of my letters to him, the patient cut off my address from it and had kept it ever since. I readily recalled my correspondence with this Australian colleague, who was very much interested in the problem of schizophrenia. Thus I suddenly learned that he had thought of getting in touch with me long before Dr. Russell had mentioned my name to him. In brief, this patient had been neurotic for many years before the war, and his friendship with the medico of his regiment was due to the fact that the latter was interested in mental mechanisms. I wish to add that most of our war neurotics belong to this class.

The well-adjusted soldier may not be fully indoctrinated into the ideals and traditions of his country, but having learned the art of war from his superiors, he empathizes himself into their mode of thinking, into their whole personality. He believes in his general, his captain and, last but not least, his sergeant.[7] Whatever one may now think of Caesar or Napoleon, their soldiers believed in them and followed them implicitly. The same situation still prevails between soldiers and their officers; it is libidinal in nature and has its origin in the father-son relation. The sergeant, as far as I could discover, usually stands for the older brother and the captain for the father, while the general stands for the early infantile father who, as we know, forms the precipitate of the superego. In other words, we deal with deep identifications which if properly managed tend to prevent war neuroses. The basis of the *esprit de corps* or so-called army *morale* is perforce a libidinal structure. Wherever this is lacking, even if it is not the only effective factor, neuroses invariably supervene. "Prussian militarism," says Freud, "which was just as unpsychological as German science, has perhaps been forced to experience that in the great World War. The war neuroses which ravaged the German army have, as is known,

[7] Cf. Brill: "The Empathic Index and Personality," *Medical Record*, January 24, 1920.

been recognized as a protest of the individual against the role attributed to him in the army." [8] I have seen many so-called war neurotics, both during the last and this war, and those I was able to study showed a marked infantile fixation and could rarely maintain themselves in an unprotected environment.

The two prominent features in the common traumatic neurosis are, first, that the chief causative factor lies in the element of surprise, or fright, and, second, that an injury or wound, suffered at the same time, usually precludes or lessens the development of the neurosis. Another noteworthy characteristic of this neurosis is found in the fact that the patient's dreams repeatedly hark back to the scene of the accident, so that he invariably awakens with renewed fright. The patient is, as it were, psychically fixed to the trauma. But fixations on disease-producing experiences have long been known in hysteria. In their first paper, Breuer and Freud said that the *hysteric suffers mostly* from reminiscences.[9] The same situation was also found in the war neuroses by Ferenczi, Jones, and Simmel.[10]

But if we accept the wish-fulfillment theory of dreams, we would expect that such patients would dream of pleasant scenes that formed part of their former healthy existence instead of the situations that provoked their neuroses. The dreams of traumatic neurotics thus contradict not only the wish-fulfilling tendencies of dreams but the "theory of psychoanalysis which definitely assumes that the course of mental processes is automatically regulated by the pleasure principle." [11]

To explain this contradiction, Freud turned his attention to the earliest normal activities of childhood, namely, playing, and reported a spontaneously invented game of a boy of one and a half years. It so happened that I visited him soon after he had finished these observations on his own grandchild, and I was fortunate enough to discuss his results with him. Since he had fully de-

---

[8] *Massenpsychologie und Ich-Analyse,* p. 49, Internat. Psychoanalyt. Verlag, 1919; English translation by Strachey.

[9] *Studies in Hysteria,* p. 4.

[10] *Kriegneurosen,* etc., *op. cit.*

[11] *Jenseits des Lustprinzips,* p. 1.

scribed his observations,[12] I shall only give a brief résumé of his findings.

The child was of average intelligence and his general behavior was good, but he had somehow acquired the habit of flinging repeatedly all his toys, as well as any small objects that he could obtain, into the corner of a room or under the bed so that it was no easy task to collect them. He seemed to evince much satisfaction in these acts, emitting a loud, long-drawn-out sound "O-O-O-Oh" every time he flung the objects away from himself. It was quite apparent to his mother and grandfather that this interjection signified "away" or "gone." Freud concluded that this was a game and that the child utilized all his toys to play "being away," or rather the game of disappearing and returning. The meaning of the play was quite clear. The child tried to overcome the annoyance caused to him whenever his mother went away and he was forced to remain home without her. He recompensed himself, as it were, for this deprivation by enacting her disappearance and return with the objects accessible to him. This interpretation was fully confirmed by another observation. One day when the mother was away for many hours, she was greeted by the child on her return with the utterance, "Baby O-O-O-Oh!" It turned out that during her long absence the child found a way to make himself disappear. He had discovered a reflection of his image in a long mirror standing on the floor and by crouching down his reflection was "away" or "gone."

Speculating on this dramatization of the child's painful experience, Freud felt that it agreed with the psychoanalytic theory that the course of any mental process is automatically regulated by the pleasure principle; that is, that it is always stimulated by a painful tension and then takes such a course that its end result coincides with a diminution of the tension, or an avoidance of pain and a production of pleasure.[13] In other words, Freud thought that the real object of the child's game was to enact the pleasurable return. But as the going away was played even more often than the second part, he concluded that there was another motive for

12 *Ibid.*, p. 12.
13 *Ibid.*, p. 1.

the playing. Instead of passively tolerating the absence of his mother, the child actively utilized the experience as a game. "This effort," says Freud, "could be ascribed to the mastery impulse [*Bemächtigungstrieb*] which expresses itself regardless of whether the memory as such is pleasurable or not." [14] The throwing away of the object may also be interpreted as a gratification of a repressed revenge fantasy against the mother, as if to say, "Yes, you can go away, I don't need you, I am sending you away myself." A year after this game had been started, the child used to fling away toys that displeased him and say, "Go to war." He knew that his father was away in the war and he did not seem to miss him, and showed most clearly that he did not wish to be disturbed in the sole possession of his mother. When I first saw this boy he was almost six years old; his mother had died and he seemed perfectly unconcerned about it. His grandfather, in discussing with me the previously described observations, ascribed the boy's lack of grief to repression.

Without following the temptation to quote more of this fascinating study, which is accessible to even those who cannot read the original, I wish to call attention to the fact that after considering the phenomena of traumatic neuroses and his observations of children's games, Freud felt convinced that even under the domination of the pleasure principle there are sufficient ways and means "to make what is in itself displeasurable as an object of memory and of psychic elaboration." He adds that an economically-minded theory of esthetics might occupy itself with these cases and situations which end in pleasure-gain. "They are of no use to us," he states, "for they presuppose the existence and domination of the pleasure principle and do not show the effect of tendencies *beyond the pleasure principle*, that is, of tendencies which might be of earlier origin and independent of it." [15]

Since Freud still entertained some doubts concerning the validity of this new concept, he confirmed it by another phenomenon. In a paper on the technique of psychoanalysis which he had written years before, he discussed memory, repetition, and elaboration as

[14] *Ibid.*, p. 14.
[15] *Ibid.*, p. 15.

they manifest themselves during the treatment.[16] In enumerating the far-reaching changes the technique has undergone since its beginning, he stated that, unlike the direct recollections that were reproduced in the cathartic therapy, we frequently find that the patient *remembers* nothing of the repressed material but acts it out instead. As Freud put it: "He does not reproduce it as a memory but as an act; he *repeats* it, without naturally knowing that he is repeating it."

Let me illustrate this by one of my cases: An hysterical young lady started her treatment by coming late for her appointments. She finally explained that, as misfortune would have it, she invariably saw someone near the building where I have my office just as she was about to enter it, and since she did not wish anyone to know that she was my patient, she had to walk at least once around the block before the entrance was free. As this continued almost daily for weeks, I began to suspect that the young lady was somewhat paranoid. But one day I discovered that her behavior expressed her resistance against telling me anything about her sexual life. For her repeated excuses were that since psychoanalysis is associated with sex, she feared lest someone seeing her near my office would think there was something wrong with her sexual life. Further questioning also showed that the first letter of the name of my apartment—Laurelton—was the same as the first letter of the word "lavatory," the name always used in her family for the bathroom. Her sexual sensitiveness began early in her life, in the lavatory, and as she grew older she was always very secretive about entering a bathroom. In brief, instead of recounting to me her first sexual trauma which occurred in the bathroom, she unconsciously "acted out" her secret through her timid and clandestine approach to my office.

Freud showed that such compulsive repetitions are intimately connected with the transference and resistance and, as every analyst knows, the transference phenomenon is in itself a bit of repetition of the past which is not only displaced to the physician

---

[16] "Erinnern, Wiederholen, und Durcharbeiten," *Internat. Ztschr. f. ärztl. Psychoanal.*, vol. II, 1914.

but to all the other current situations of the patient's life. As Freud states: "This reproduction which appears with undesired fidelity always contains a fragment of the infantile sexual life, that is, of the Oedipus complex and its offshoots, and is regularly enacted in the spheres of the transference, that is, in the relation to the physician." [17] As to its relation to the pleasure principle, Freud states that "the repetition compulsion also reproduces such past experiences that contain no possibility of pleasure and could at no time have been a source of gratification." [18] Thus by virtue of the fact that the child's wishes are incompatible with reality, and because of the inadequacy of the infantile stage of development, the infantile sexual life is destined to decline and perish under the most painful circumstances and profound feelings of pain. The tender bonds which the child feels mostly for the parent of the opposite sex must succumb to disappointment. In addition, there is the jealousy at the birth of another child, the yoke of discipline and education—all these unwished-for experiences with their painful affects are later repeated by neurotics in their transference.[19]

But the same repetition compulsion which is observed in neurotic transference is also seen in so-called normals. In the latter it gives the impression of a "pursuing fate," of which so many people complain, but which is demonstrated by analysis as being mostly self-imposed on the basis of infantile influences. These observations from the neurotic transference and from the so-called "fate" in normals justified the assumption of a repetition compulsion in psychic life which goes beyond the pleasure principle. According to Freud, the dreams of traumatic or war neuroses, as well as the play of children, belong in the same category, but the repetition compulsion seems to be "more primitive, more elementary and more instinctive than the pleasure principle which it has shoved aside." "But," continues Freud, "if there is such a repetition compulsion in psychic life, we should like to know something about it,

[17] *Jenseits des Lustprinzips*, p. 16.
[18] *Ibid.*, p. 18.
[19] *Ibid.*, p. 19.

to what functions it corresponds, under what conditions it may appear and in what relation it stands to the pleasure principle, to which we have hitherto ascribed the domination over the course of excitation process in the psychic life." [20]

[20] *Ibid.*, p. 21.

THIRTEEN

REPETITION COMPULSION, CONSCIOUS-NESS, AND INSTINCT

"WHAT now follows is speculation which each one will credit or disregard according to his particular attitude. Broadly, it is an attempt of a consistent exploitation of an idea, out of curiosity, whither this will lead." [1]

With these remarks Freud begins the fourth chapter of *Jenseits des Lustprinzips*. For in contrast to the first three chapters, which deal with clinical material which every experienced psychoanalyst can easily follow, the last four chapters are devoted to material that is more or less new to psychoanalytic thinking. Having assumed the phenomenon of repetition compulsion, Freud now proceeds to test its validity by co-ordinating it with the functions of consciousness and with the manifestations of the instinct.

He begins by reviewing what he had repeatedly said about the system of consciousness and its various strata. He emphasized the fact that consciousness is not the most common character of the psychic processes but only a special function of the same; that it is essentially a receptive organ for impression from the outer world and for the feelings of pleasure and pain emanating from the inner psychic apparatus. He conjectures that: "It must lie between the outer and inner boundaries, turned toward the outer world, and that it must cover the other psychic systems." [2] Consciousness is not, however, the only peculiarity attributed to the processes in this system. For we know from psychoanalysis that all excitation processes leave permanent traces in the other systems as memory remnants which have nothing to do with becoming conscious. These are often strongest and most tenacious if the process that left them behind never attains consciousness. Hence, one could say that a process of excitation in this system produces conscious-

[1] *Ibid.*, p. 22.
[2] *Ibid.*, p. 22.

ness but does not leave behind any permanent trace, and that whatever memory it produces is due to a diffusion of the excitation into the nearest inner systems. Freud follows here the scheme he formulated in the speculative part of his *Interpretation of Dreams*, and then states: "If one thinks how little we know from other sources about the origin of consciousness, one must concede at least the importance of a more or less definite statement to the principle: *consciousness arises in the place of memory traces.*

"The system of consciousness would thus be distinguished by the peculiarity that stimuli do not leave a permanent change in its elements as in all other psychic systems, but that they vanish, as it were, in the phenomenon of becoming conscious." [3] Freud explains this deviation by one factor, which is exclusively present in this one system and in none of the others, namely, by the exposed position of the system of consciousness, or by its immediate contact with the outer world. Because of its position, it becomes differentiated and serves as a receptive organ for stimuli or excitations from the outer world as well as for feelings of pleasure and pain emanating from within the psychic apparatus or from the instincts. [4]

Freud goes on to say that the continuous impact of the outer stimuli on this surface would produce a permanent change in its substance up to a certain depth, so that processes of excitation would take a different course in this layer than in the deeper strata. It could form a crust which would finally be so thoroughly enkindled from the effects of stimuli that it would offer the most favorable soil for their reception but would be incapable of further modification. Applied to the system of consciousness, it would mean that its elements could not become more permanently changed through the passage of excitation because they had already attained the optimum capacity of this effect, yet they would be capable of giving rise to consciousness.

Having associated, albeit speculatively, the origin of consciousness with the position of the system of consciousness, and with the peculiarities of the excitation processes attributed to it, Freud then

[3] *Ibid.*, p. 23.
[4] *Ibid.*, p. 24.

conjectures that this fragment of living substance, exposed to the outer world and charged with the strongest energies, would be destroyed by these stimuli if it were not equipped with a *stimulus barrier* (*Reizschutz*). This barrier came into being because the outermost surface of the system of consciousness gave up, as it were, its living structure and in a measure became inorganic. It thus serves as a special integument or membrane for warding off stimuli, that is, for preventing the energies of the outer world from exerting more than a bit of its intensity on the next still more vital layers. The latter, lying behind the stimulus barrier, can now devote themselves to the reception of the masses of stimuli that pass through it, and thus learn the direction and nature of the outer stimuli. In the higher organisms the stimulus-receiving, crusted stratum had long ago receded into the inner depth of the body, leaving only small portions of it on the surface under the imme- diate protection of the stimulus barrier. These sensory organs are characterized by the fact that they assimilate only a small quantity of external stimuli. They accept only specimens from the outer world, and may perhaps be compared to feelers that grope around in the external world and then always retract from it.[5]

In brief, consciousness is a receptive organ which by virtue of its gradual evolution acts, as it were, as a barrier against excitations from without, but not against stimuli emanating from within. The stimuli of the deeper layers continue to flow, directly and in un- diminished quantity, into the system, while certain characteristics of their course produce the series of pleasure-pain feelings. To be sure, the excitations emanating from them, depending on their intensity and other qualitative characteristics, are more adequate than those streaming in from the outer world. However, two things are definitely discerned in these relations. First, a preponder- ance over all outer stimuli of the pleasure-pain feelings, which are an index for the processes within the apparatus, and, second, a trend of behavior toward those inner excitations which carry an excess of pain. To afford them the protection of the stimulus barrier, there is a tendency to treat them as if they came from without rather than from within. "This," says Freud, "is the origin of *pro-*

[5] *Ibid.*, p. 26.

jection which is destined to play such a great part in the causation of pathologic processes." [6]

As all these reflections have only given a better understanding of the domination of the pleasure principle and offered no explanation of those cases that contradict it, Freud goes a step farther and asserts that: "Such excitations from without which are strong enough to cause a break through the stimulus barrier we call traumatic." [7] He adds that the concept of trauma expresses such a relationship to an otherwise efficient stimulus barrier. A trauma coming from without will surely provoke an extensive disturbance in the energy functions of the organism; it will mobilize all defense measures, and thus put out of action the pleasure principle. The psychic apparatus becomes flooded with large masses of stimuli, and the resulting task is to control them, that is, to bind them psychically, and then bring them to discharge. After discussing the specific mechanisms caused by breaches in the protective barrier, Freud states that "the ordinary traumatic neurosis is the result of an extensive breach in the stimulus barrier." [8]

This view, though stressing the importance of the fright and threat to life rather than the effect of mechanical violence, takes note also of the old "shock theory." [9] For the latter considers the nature of shock as a direct injury to the molecular structure, or even to the histologic structure of the nerve elements, while psychoanalysis seeks to understand the effect of the breach in the stimulus barrier on the psychic organ, as well as the problems resulting from it.

Freud now returns to the above-mentioned contradiction to the wish-fulfillment theory of dreams and states: "When the dreams of traumatic neurotic patients take them so regularly back to the situation of the accident, they do not by any means thereby serve

[6] *Ibid.*, p. 27.
[7] *Ibid.*, p. 27.
[8] *Ibid.*, p. 29.
[9] Freud differentiates between *fright*, *fear* and *anxiety* in their relation to danger. *Fright* describes the state of a person who is suddenly confronted by danger for which he is unprepared; the element of surprise is most important here. *Fear* requires a definite object of which one is afraid, while *anxiety* designates a state in which one expects danger and is prepared for it.

the aim of wish fulfillment, the hallucinatory induction of which has, under the domination of the pleasure principle, become its function. But we must assume that they thereby put themselves at the disposal of another task, the solution of which must be accomplished before the pleasure principle can begin its sway. These dreams strive to restore the control over the stimuli by developing anxiety, the absence of which was the cause of the traumatic neurosis. They thus afford us a view into the function of the psychic apparatus which, without contradicting the pleasure principle, nevertheless seems to be independent of it, and of earlier origin than the aim of gaining pleasure and avoiding pain." [10]

Freud admits here, for the first time, an exception to the rule that a dream represents the realization of a wish, but adds that neither "anxiety" nor "punishment dreams" form this exception. The latter merely present the appropriate punishment in place of the forbidden wish realization, and thus represent the wish fulfillment of the sense of guilt, which is a reaction to the rejected impulse. But the dreams of traumatic neurotics, as well as the dreams that reproduce psychic traumas, can no longer be brought under the category of wish fulfillment.[11] They obey rather the repetition compulsion which is supported in analysis by the (not unconscious) wish to bring up again what has been forgotten and repressed. Thus the effort of the dream to remove the motives for interrupting sleep, by wish fulfillment of the disturbing impulses, would not be its original function. The dream could assume control over this function only after the whole psychic life had accepted the domination of the pleasure principle. For if there is a "beyond the pleasure principle," it is logical to concede a past age also to the wish-fulfilling tendency of dreams. In other words, such dreams follow the repetition-compulsion phenomenon and merely strive to bind psychically traumatic experiences.

Having presented Freud's concept of traumatic neuroses, I shall now add also his conclusions on the war neuroses which, as noted

---

[10] *Ibid.*, p. 30.
[11] Cf. also Freud: *Neue Folge der Vorlesungen*, p. 23, Internat. Psychoanal. Verlag; English translation *New Introductory Lectures on Psychoanalysis,* W. W. Norton and Co.

previously, are really traumatic neuroses favored by an ego conflict. As we have seen, a severe injury occurring simultaneously
with the trauma lessens the chances for the origin of the neuroses.
This can be easily understood if one bears in mind two facts emphasized in psychoanalytic investigation: first, that mechanical
excitations "by means of rhythmic mechanical shaking of the
body" produce sexual stimulation [12] and, second, that painful and
feverish diseases exert a strong influence on the distribution of the
libido. The mechanical force of the trauma thus sets free a quantity
of sexual excitation which, lacking any preparation for anxiety,
acts traumatically, while the simultaneously occurring physical injury binds the excess of excitement by the demand of a narcistic
overcathexis of the injured organ.[13] For it is also known that even
so severe a disturbance in the libido distribution as exists in melancholia may be removed through an intercurrent organic disease;
indeed, that even a fully developed schizophrenia is capable of a
transitory improvement under similar conditions.[14]

Having disposed of the problem of traumatic and war neuroses,
Freud now compares the possible effects of a trauma with the
instinctual excitations of living substances. He begins with the
statement that the lack of a stimulus barrier against excitations
from within necessarily causes these transmissions of stimuli to
acquire a greater economic importance, and frequently gives rise
to economic disturbances which can be compared to traumatic
neuroses. "The most prolific sources of such inner excitations are
the so-called instincts of the organism, the representatives of all
forces arising within the body and transmitted to the psychic apparatus." [15] These excitations do not belong to the "bound" but to
the freely moving nerve processes striving for discharge. All that

[12] *Three Contributions to the Theory of Sex,* in *Freud's Basic Writings,*
p. 600.

[13] Freud: "Zur Einführung des Narzismus," *Neurosenlehre,* 4th Series,
p. 78, 1918.

[14] This statement was made long before "shock therapy" was known; it
explains also the temporary improvements that have been noted occasionally
in schizophrenics who undergo surgical operations. Cf. Brill: "A Case of
Schizophrenia," *Am. J. Insanity,* July, 1909.

[15] *Jenseits des Lustprinzips,* p. 32.

is known concerning these processes was gleaned from the study of the "Dream-Work," [16] in which Freud designates this kind of process in the unconscious as the "primary process," in contradistinction to the secondary process which is effective in normal waking life. As all the instinctive stimuli affect the unconscious systems, one may say that they follow the primary process; that is, they represent an unbound, freely moving cathexis which has to be mastered by the psychic apparatus. A failure of this binding would provoke a disturbance similar to a traumatic neurosis, and only after they have been successfully bound can the domination of the pleasure principle (and its modification, the reality principle) proceed unhindered. "But till then," states Freud, "the other task of the psychic apparatus, the impulsion to sway or to bind, predominates, to be sure not in opposition to the pleasure principle, but independent of it, and, in part, without regard to it." [17]

This independence of the pleasure principle expresses itself in its obedience to the repetition compulsion, as described above in the early activities of childhood—playing—(see p. 211), and in the transference manifestations during psychoanalytic treatment. But to comprehend in one principle all these clinical experiences, it is necessary to find "in what way the instinctive is connected with the compulsion to repetition." Freud answers this question by saying that: "Here an idea is forced upon us, that we came upon the track of a general, hitherto not clearly recognized, character of the instincts, perhaps of all organic life. *An instinct would thus be an urge innate in living organic matter toward the reinstatement of an earlier state*, which this living organic matter had to give up under the influence of external disturbing forces. It is a kind of organic elasticity, or if you will, the manifestation of the inertia in organic life." [18]

Since I cannot give here a complete review of this very fascinating, albeit speculative, work, I must stop at this point. I shall

[16] Cf. ch. VI, *The Interpretation of Dreams*, in *Freud's Basic Writings*, p. 319.
[17] *Ibid.*, p. 33.
[18] *Ibid.*, p. 34.

merely add that in this work Freud lays the foundation for his next book, *The Ego and the Id,* wherein he fully discusses the strata of the psychic apparatus and the life and death instincts.[19]

I wondered why I had given so much space to Freud's concept of the traumatic neuroses which I now realize could have been condensed into a few paragraphs. "Free associations" immediately recalled a letter from Freud (December 26, 1939) which I received after he had first seen a copy of the omnibus of his basic writings. He said: *"Die Basic Writings* haben mich sehr erfreut. Mit Bedauern fand ich aber die 3 theoretischen Essays (*Lustprinzip, Massenpsychologie, Ich und Es*) ausgeschlossen. Aber Sie müssen gute Gründe gehabt haben, und Ihre ausgezeichnete Einleitung geht doch auf dieses Stück der Lehre ein." (I was very much pleased with the *Basic Writings.* But I was sorry to find that you have not included the three theoretical essays [*Pleasure Principle, Mass Psychology, Ego and Id*]. But you must have had good reasons, and your excellent introduction does enter into this part of the theory.) I did not include these three works in the *Basic Writings* because they were not translated by me. Nevertheless, Freud's wish to have them there must have unconsciously guided me to insert this rather long interlude in the present work.[20] I do think, however, that the reader will not be hurt by gaining some insight into Freud's metapsychological mode of thinking.

[19] Cf. Brill: "The Death Instinct in Relation to Normal and Abnormal Life," *Medical Leaves,* Chicago, 1937.

[20] Dr. Geza Roheim, the anthropological psychoanalyst who happened to call on me while I was writing the above, immediately characterized my behavior as a "nachträglichen Gehorsam," or a subsequent obedience of sons toward fathers. Cf. *Totem and Taboo,* in *Freud's Basic Writings,* p. 917.

FOURTEEN

THE PALEOPSYCHOLOGIST OF THE MIND

In a letter dated December 4, 1938, Freud wrote: "Mein nächstes Buch wird im Frühjahr erscheinen (*Moses und die monotheistische Religion*) auch in einer amerikanischen Ausgabe. Seither hat meine Production geruht." (My next book will appear in the spring [*Moses and Monotheism*] also in an American edition. Since then my productions have rested.)

In these words Freud announced the epitome of all his productions. As was his habit, he first published two separate papers[1] which now form Parts I and II of his last work, and he would have undoubtedly published the third paper before incorporating it as Part III of *Moses and Monotheism* had he not been interrupted by the Nazi terror which forced him to emigrate to London. He therefore wrote his last and most interesting work in exile. The importance of this work, which was unjustly criticized, lies in the fact that Freud bridges here the gap between the individual and the race. In tracing neurotic disturbances to earliest childhood, Freud demonstrated that all later adjustment of the individual depends on his early reaction to the Oedipus complex. The latter is a universal phenomenon which, as shown by dreams of children and adults, must have always existed. But as with the individual, the race, too, had its Oedipus complex. In the myth, Oedipus killed his father and married his mother; in modern life this complex manifests itself in dreams of the father's death, whereas in prehistoric society this wish was actually effected through the slaying and devouring of the primeval father by his rebellious sons. And just as the moral standards of the individual are determined by his reaction to the Oedipus complex, Freud traces religion and other moral and social institutions to that earliest of all dramas. In a most interesting and convincing manner, he depicts the his-

---

[1] *Imago*, 1937; in English, in the *Internat. J. Psycho-Anal.*, July, 1938, and January, 1939, respectively.

torical and emotional bases of monotheism on the scheme of a traumatic neurosis. He frankly admits that his prehistorical survey leaves many gaps which cannot possibly be bridged, but, as shown above (see p. 189), there is considerable evidence for his assumptions. His greatest difficulty was encountered in his attempt to translate individual into mass psychology. For in the neurosis the memory traces of the traumatic event continue to exist in the individual's unconscious, and can be brought to light by analysis. But all kinds of complications arise when one attempts to show how an active tradition exists in the life of a people.

It would lead me far away from my goal if I were to attempt to follow the steps taken by Freud in his fascinating elucidations. In brief, Freud concludes that the psyche of man consists not only of personal experiences but also of what he brought with him at birth. That is to say, the mind contains also fragments of phyletic origin, or better, an *archaic inheritance*, which consists of certain dispositions common to all living beings—in the ability and tendency to follow a certain trend of development and in a special mode of reaction to excitations and stimuli. Experience shows that individuals differ in this respect and that these differences are determined by the *archaic inheritance*. They represent what we recognize in the individual as *constitutional* elements. In other words, the archaic heritage of mankind includes not only dispositions but also ideational contents, unconscious memory traces of experiences of former generations. Freud maintains "in all modesty" that despite those biologists who reject the view of the transmissibility of acquired characteristics, he cannot picture biological development without taking this factor into account.

If we recall the general characteristics Freud attributed to instincts, his attitude on the question of inheritance of acquired characteristics is not surprising. This is, however, his first direct expression on this important biological problem. Here he openly joins the ranks of Darwin, Hering, Haeckel, Butler, Semon, Bleuler and many others who expressed similar views. But having closed the gap between individual and race psychology, Freud states: "After these considerations, I have no qualms in saying that men have always known—in this particular way—that once upon a time they had a primeval father and killed him." [2]

Thus everything Freud expressed from the beginning of his collaboration with Breuer to the present day can be epitomized as follows: The child begins with an *id* psyche, a part of which gradually becomes molded and modified into an *ego*. This ego, having developed cognition of the dangers threatening the organism from without, henceforth strives to curb the id tendencies for its own protection. Everything being equal, and as a result of continuous struggle with the outer world, a part of the ego gradually becomes modified into a *superego*. This super or ideal ego represents the highest attainment in the mental evolution of man. The race, which has been subjected throughout the ages to the same trials and vicissitudes as the individual, seems to have reacted to emotional experiences as has the individual. The id psyche remains unchanged; the ego is forever in the midst of the struggle between the id and the outer world, while the superego plays the same part in the individual as in the race. In the individual it represents the earthly father while in the race the Father in Heaven. Conflicts between these psychic forces produce neuroses and psychoses in the individual and psychic upheavals in the race.

In *Moses and Monotheism* Freud unified the primordial past with the historical present. Like Spinoza, to whom I like to compare him, he, too, looked at everything *sub specie aeternitatis*, under the guise of eternity. Freud was the first student of the mind to demonstrate clinically the truth of the old Greek maxims "Know thyself" and "Man is the measure of all things." Unlike his predecessors who looked upon the neurotic and the psychotic as fragmentary, isolated monstrosities, as something foreign to the rest of life, Freud, with his Januslike vision, perceived them as the most fascinating phenomena of civilization. Through them and them alone he solved the sphinxlike riddle of struggling mankind. What Darwin did for biology, Freud did for psychology. Highly endowed by an oriental heritage and a Western environment, he could venture into the deepest recesses of the psyche and wrest from it its hidden secrets.

[2] *Moses and Monotheism*, p. 159.

A year after the publication of the *Studien über Hysterie* he presented the first complete formulation of his life's task in an address before the Vienna Society of Psychiatry and Neurology. Comparing the methods hitherto pursued in the examination of neurotics with his own, he said: "Let us assume that a traveling investigator came to a region hardly known, where his interest was arrested by ruins of the remains of walls, fragments of pillars, and tablets showing blurred and illegible inscriptions. He could be satisfied with a superficial examination of the things lying before him and with questioning the semibarbaric natives living near by about what tradition tells concerning the history and meaning of those monumental remains, note the information, and then continue his journey. But he could also proceed differently. He could have brought along picks, shovels, and spades, employ the inhabitants to attack with these tools the ruins, to clear away the debris and to uncover the visible remains of what had been buried. If the efforts of his labor are rewarded, the findings then explain themselves. The wall remnants belong to the rampart of a palace or treasure house; the ruined pillars form part of a temple, the numerous inscriptions, which are fortunately bilingual, disclose an alphabet and a language, the deciphering and translation of which yield unimaginable disclosures about events of the past, to the commemoration of which these monuments were built. *Saxa loquuntur!*" [3]

The biological researcher who devoted so many years to the study of the nervous system of the lowly fish *Amoecetes petromyzon* thus compared himself to an archaeologist or paleontologist who patiently clears away the rubbish of centuries to lay bare an old temple or the remains of a prehistoric monster. About four years later in the preface to *The Dora Case*, which represents the first model of a psychoanalytic case history, he actually demonstrated how this *modus operandi* is applicable to patients. For he states: "In view of the incompleteness of my analytic results, there was nothing left to me but to follow the examples of those discoverers who are fortunate enough to bring to light, from their long burial, the priceless, even though mutilated, relics of antiquity. I

[3] *Neurosenlehre*, I, 150.

have restored the missing parts according to the best models from other analyses known to me. But like the conscientious archaeologist, I have not failed to mention, in each case, where my constructions are added to the authentic parts." [4]

Those who are well versed in Freud's psychoanalytic theories find his paleopsychological reconstructions rational and quite simple. Delving into the unconscious of a neurotic may be justly compared to the painstaking and protracted work of the archaeologist or paleontologist. It calls for, according to Freud who expressed it in Goethe's words,

> Nicht Kunst und Wissenschaft allein,
> Geduld will bei dem Werke sein!

(It requires not only art and science but also patience!)

The analogy between archaeology and psychoanalysis seems to have especially appealed to Freud. Thus in his "Reflection on War and Death" [5] he states: "When a town becomes a city or a child grows into a man, town and child disappear in the city and in the man. Only memory can sketch in the old features in the new picture; in reality the old materials and forms have been replaced by new ones. It is different in the case of psychic evolution." He then goes on to state that in psychic evolution every previous stage of development is preserved next to the following one, from which it has been evolved. The succession stipulates a coexistence although the changed material remains the same. The earlier psychic state may remain dormant for years but it continues to exist and may someday again assume the upper hand and cause, as it were, an annulment and regression of all the subsequent developments. Sometimes a later and higher stage of development that has been abandoned cannot be attained again. "But," adds Freud, "the primitive conditions can always be reconstructed; the primitive psyche is in the strictest sense indestructible." [6]

Freud thus shows the difference between archaeology and hu-

---

[4] *Ibid.*, II, 20.
[5] *Ibid.*, p. 30.
[6] *Ibid.*, p. 32.

man paleontology which Smith Ely Jelliffe aptly calls paleopsy-
chology. Following years of preparation Freud then spent over
half a century to produce this new science. To do so he ventured
into fields hitherto undiscovered. No one before him has shown
how human beings actually feel and think. Many others before
him have sensed much that Freud later discovered on the basis of
clinical material, but it was his great merit to embody all these
parts into one imposing structure. The therapy itself is perhaps
the most insignificant part of Freud's discoveries. It is, however,
in comparison to the other psychotherapies, the most logical scientific and true mental therapy. Psychoanalytic therapy has been
more or less justly criticized because it is not as fast, not as pleasant
and not as cheap as sugar-coated pills. As an earnest student of
the neuroses and psychoses for over forty years *I know that there
are no short cuts to the cure of mental diseases.* "Shocking" therapies may change patients temporarily for better or worse,[7] and
gouging out part of their brains may restrict their functional
activities, but those therapies *do not cure* and are no improvement
on the many similar panaceas that preceded them and flickered
out. As that old sage, Smith Ely Jelliffe, speaking of lobectomy,
puts it: "The man with the amputated leg may use a wooden one,
or a crutch, or a wheel-chair, but where are these homologues to
be found for the partly decapitated human being?" [8]

If there is any truth in the homeopathic formula *similia similibus
curantur* it is certainly applicable to psychotherapy, in the sense
that mental and emotional disturbances can only be alleviated and
cured by mental procedures. Lest I be misunderstood I hasten to
add that psychoanalysis cannot cure everything. Neither Freud
nor any of his pupils have ever made such claims.[9] It is true that
treatment by *Freud's* psychoanalysis is a lengthy process. But
someday either some wise and generous philanthropist, if there
will be any, or a wise and benign government will endow psycho-

[7] Cf. Brill: "The Etiological Relationship of Trauma to Schizophrenia,"
Medical Record, March, 1941.

[8] Jelliffe: "Some notes on Parathyroid Dysfunction," *Medical Record*, December, 1942.

[9] Cf Brill: "A Psychoanalyst Scans His Past," *J. Nerv. and Ment. Dis.*, May,
1942.

analytic clinics and hospitals and thus make such treatment accessible to everybody.

Other criticism against Freud's psychoanalysis was expressed recently in an editorial of the *Journal of the American Medical Association*.[10] Most of the writer's implied objections to psychoanalysis are hardly worthy of an editorial. Thus he quoted a sentence of two lines from some psychoanalytic author which he could not understand and, therefore, stated that such a sentence "is without value to the uninitiated, and its real significance even to those actively working in the field may be questioned." I am sure that I have not written this sentence, and I admit that I do not understand it either, but just for fun I picked out a sentence from the next editorial and although I am a constant reader of the *Journal* I couldn't understand it at all. Indeed, the whole editorial on "Detoxication By Liver Extracts" was unintelligible to me. However, I explained my ignorance to a lack of knowledge of modern chemistry and physiology and have not sought to cast aspersions on those who specialize in these fields and write about them learnedly.

The objectionable sentence contains the word "cathexis" which may have confused the editor. To be sure, this term was coined by psychoanalysts, but as it has been fully explained and is found in all standard dictionaries, there is no need apologizing for it. Freud has added many new words to all modern languages. As he discovered new phenomena he had to coin new expressions for them. As I see it, Freud started by collecting isolated facts which he then combined into great wholes in order to discover general laws, and as time went on, these wholes illumined the otherwise single facts and thus explained them. As he could not work out all these things in a laboratory, his deductions must be considered in the light of any other excursion into the realm of paleontology where, for example *ex ossiculo Dinosauria*, a whole species of prehistoric beasts were reconstructed long before Roy Chapman Andrews discovered their eggs with well-developed embryos. Everything new must begin with speculation, but Freud has always started with clinical material, and it is important to note that his

[10] July 17, 1943.

results have later been confirmed by many others. His discoveries have not yet been properly evaluated. We are still too close to the mountain to obtain a true perspective of its grandeur. But having followed Freud's productions as they appeared in rapid succession and having noted their effects on our times I can only repeat that his discoveries mark the greatest epoch in the mental sciences. Freud has revolutionized our whole approach to the study of the mind. New schools of thought have rapidly sprung up in psychology, in anthropology, in sociology, in pedagogics and in belles-lettres. Even Freud's former opponents are now taking note of psychogenesis, dream analysis, and sex in studying their patients. Thomas Mann summed up the feeling of many modern littérateurs when he called Freud "the greatest living man of letters whose discoveries pointed the way to an art which might be bolder, freer, blither, than any possible in our neurotic, fear-ridden, hate-ridden world." [11]

Much could also be said about the present and future status of psychoanalysis in this country. But having set out to present here Freud's contribution to psychiatry, I feel that my task has been accomplished. Judging from my own observations I can say that psychoanalysis has benefited not only psychiatry but all the other medical disciplines as well. Yet one cannot say that there have been any new and significant discoveries since Freud. It will take considerable time before we will assimilate what the master left us. Many books and papers are continually appearing in psychoanalytic and other publications; some are very good, some are not so valuable, but it is still difficult to say what is a mere elaboration on one of Freud's concepts and what is an original contribution. Living in the midst of war it occurs to me that the Freudian analysts are in the position of an army that is consolidating its position in a still hostile country. They are, so to say, reorganizing their ranks and gradually eliminating the weak and the infirm from their midst. Meanwhile psychoanalysis is making excursions and incursions into other fields of medicine, the most promising of which are child study and psychosomatic medicine. The im-

[11] Thomas Mann: *Freud and the Future,* New York, Alfred A. Knopf, 1939.

portance of childhood has been emphasized by Freud and his pupils from the very beginning of the psychoanalytic movement but for the last two decades this has also been recognized by pedagogy and psychology. That the soma and the psyche are inseparable and are mutually dependent has been known to analysis as it was to the ancients, but it is only through Freud's teaching that the medical profession is now realizing its importance and actually taking note of it. In Plato's dialogue *Charmides*, Socrates quotes the Thracian king's physician as criticizing the Greek physicians because they were attempting to cure the body without curing the mind. "This," he said, "is the reason why the cure of many diseases is unknown to the physicians of Hellas; they are ignorant of the whole." "For this," he continued, "is the great error of our day in the treatment of the human body, that physicians separate the mind from the body." Socrates then added: "Hence if the body is to be well, one must begin by curing the mind. And the cure, my dear youth, has to be effected by the use of certain charms, and these charms *are fair words*." [12] Socrates thus anticipated the value of Breuer's "talking cure" out of which Freud made psychoanalysis. Dr. Smith Ely Jelliffe was the pioneer in psychosomatic medicine [13] in this country. Like Groddek abroad, Jelliffe stressed here the psychic elements in organic diseases. The present interest in psychosomatic medicine is thus due directly to psychoanalysis, and indirectly to those farsighted physicians and surgeons who recognized the importance of psychogenetic factors in organic diseases.

Ewald Hering ends his classical lecture on memory as a general function of organized matter [14] in the following words: "Man's conscious memory comes to an end with his death; but the unconscious memory of nature is true and ineradicable. Whoever succeeds in stamping upon it the impress of his work will be remembered forever."

Whatever modifications and amplifications some of Freud's con-

[12] *Italicized by the author.*
[13] *Sketches in Psychosomatic Medicine*, Nervous and Mental Disease Monographs, 1939.
[14] *Über das Gedächtniss als eine allgemeine Funktion der organischen Materie*, Gerold, Wien, 1870.

cepts may in future experience from within or from without, his basic principles will always remain as the most outstanding contribution to psychiatry. Freud has established the monism of the mind, because he has wiped out the line of demarcation between normal and abnormal mentation. Instead of a restricted study of mental pathology, psychiatry is now a broad and comprehensive science which embraces all healthy and sick aspects of the mind both ontogenetically and phylogenetically.

INDEX

A

Abnormalities, and civilization, 182; sexual, 84

Abraham, Dr., 30, 98, 142, 166, 179, 207

Abreaction, 62, 174

Abstinence, sexual, 76, 77

Acromegaly, 25, 30

Affect, 97; economized expenditure of, 172; reversal of, 110; strangulated, 61

Aggression, 86, 89

Aims, pursued by the ego and id, 155; sexual and nonsexual, 85, 86; of suggestive and analytic therapy, 72

Alcohol, desire for, 177, 179

Algolagnic activities, 129

Ambivalence, 110, 116, 126, 166, 168, 180, 188

American Psychoanalytic Association, 40

Amnesia, 56; posthypnotic, 67

Anal-erotism, 141, 145, 147

Anal regression, 138

Anal-sadistic level, 133, 145, 147

Analysis, 42, 72, 91, 92, 94, 95, 103, 134, 169, 204

Andrews, Roy Chapman, 231

Anna O., case of, 53, 57, 58, 59, 60, 61

Anorexia nervosa, 166

Anthropology, 232

Anti-Semitism, 55, 192, 193, 194, 196; crypto-, 195

Anxiety, 76, 154, 209, 220, 221, 222

Aphasia, 49

Apparatus, mental, 39, 151, 152; psychic, 41, 71, 151, 152, 154, 155, 156, 223

Archaeology, and human paleontology, 229, 230; and psychoanalysis, 231

Aristotle, 62

Army, civilian, 208; morale in, 210

Art, 182, 183, 189

Aschaffenburg, 32

Associations, obsessive, 202; *see also* Free associations

Astrology, 37

Atkinson, 186

Atonement, 187; Jewish day of, 176

Auto-erotism, 84, 105, 134, 137, 141

B

Babylonia, 36

Baptism, as a salvation for Jewish disabilities, 197

Basic Writings of Sigmund Freud, 73, 78, 80, 154, 176, 224

Beard, George Miller, 76

Bellevue Hospital, psychiatric department, 63, 108

Bernays, Anna (Freud's sister), 196

Bernays, Martha, 51

Bernheim, 56, 57

Bernheim's clinic, 66

Beyond the Pleasure Principle, 151, 207, 221

Bianchi, Leonardo, 20

Bible, 186, 190, 206

Biology, 183, 227

Bisexuality, 127, 128; and the Oedipus complex, 130

Blakeslee, George A., 209

Bleuler, 13, 14, 28, 30, 32, 42, 73, 97, 98, 133, 134, 151, 183, 195, 226

Bloomingdale Hospital, 106, 107

Braid, James, 38

Breuer, Joseph, 40, 46, 53, 55, 57, 58, 60, 64, 65, 78, 205, 207, 211, 227, 233

Brill, A. A., 14, 41, 46, 50, 53, 62, 72, 78, 86, 90, 104, 133, 142, 172, 184, 203, 222, 230

Brill, Rose Owen, 5

THE THOMAS WILLIAM SALMON
MEMORIAL LECTURES

The Salmon Lectures of the New York Academy of Medicine were established in 1931, as a memorial to Thomas William Salmon, M.D., and for the advancement of the objects to which his professional career had been wholly devoted.

Dr. Salmon died in 1927, at the age of 51, after a career of extraordinary service in psychiatric practice and education, and in the development of a world-wide movement for the better treatment and prevention of mental disorders, and for the promotion of mental health.

Following his death, a group of his many friends organized a committee for the purpose of establishing one or more memorials that might serve to preserve and pass on to future generations some of the spirit and purpose of his supremely noble and useful life. Five hundred and ninety-six subscriptions were received, three hundred and nineteen from physicians.

Of the amount thus obtained, $100,000 was, on January 10, 1931, given to the New York Academy of Medicine, as a fund to provide an income for the support of an annual series of lectures and for other projects for the advancement of psychiatry and mental hygiene. For the purpose of giving lasting quality to the lectures as a memorial to Dr. Salmon, and of extending their usefulness, it was stipulated that each series should be published in a bound volume of which this volume is one.